Psilocybin Mushrooms

3 in 1: How to Grow Psychedelic Magic Mushrooms, Safe Use, and Basic Mushroom Identification

Inspirational Creator

ISBN 978-1-922940-00-1 (E-book)

ISBN 978-1-922940-01-8 (Paperback)

ISBN 978-1-922940-02-5 (Hardback)

Cover Design by DesignVibe

Published by Inspirational Creator

First Edition (2022)

Bil Harret

Table of Contents

Introduction

Welcome to the world of everything "shrooms!" If you are reading this book you are interested in their magical properties, right? Congratulations, because we will explore every aspect of them and more. Mushrooms are a controversial topic, as some deem them evil while others see them as God's gift to the human race. Regardless of your personal viewpoints, I'm quite sure you won't view magic mushrooms the same after reading this book. There's a reason they're called magic!

Although these little beauties aren't really filled with "magic," they do have an effect on the body, and ingesting them will put you on a super life-changing journey if you use them responsibly.

There are over 180 different species of mushrooms that contain Psilocybin, which has psychedelic-'mind altering'-effects, hence the name 'magic mushrooms'. The end result or your 'trip' will differ from other individuals depending on the setting and your personality.

Shrooms are generally picked and eaten raw, but you can dry them or cook with them too. Be aware, though, that heat exposure will decrease its potency as Psilocybin degrades at higher temperatures. Shrooms come in all shapes, sizes, and colors, grow in various areas including forests as well as urban areas and are quite versatile.

Shrooms are like anything else in life; if used in moderation, they can enrich your world with loads of deep, meaningful thoughts about the universe, the cosmos, and yourself. In fact, you might learn the answers to questions you've had for years!

Shrooms have even been found to play a positive role in couples therapy! Some couples have explained that, through their mushroom experience, they felt a deeper connection and an increased understanding of one another. They could "see" into each other's souls and felt an elevated physical link, something that drew them closer together. Even cuddling was a new experience as many people mentioned it felt as if they were melting into each other, becoming one!

At higher dosages, you will begin to hallucinate and 'trip', providing you with a magnificent 'Alice in Wonderland' encounter lasting up to six hours!

As with any hallucinogenic, your trip will depend on what's going on with you at that time. If you're in a negative mental state or bad environment, it's suggested to avoid psychedelics.

Magic mushrooms aren't addictive, tolerance builds up fast, and fades as fast as it builds. They can be a very safe, healthy "drug" if used responsibly. Luckily, the negative stigma of magic mushrooms is fading as scientists have started to realize they have many benefits not yet explored.

Magic mushrooms have been around for centuries. Many cultures have made use of magic mushrooms during ceremonies to enhance their spirituality and for healing purposes. They have various other potential benefits like helping break addictive habits, alleviating anxiety, reducing depression, and increasing one's creativity. New studies are being done as we speak to see if Psilocybin can be used to treat OCD, PTSD, and several mental health conditions, including eating disorders. They have been used to alleviate pain, including discomfort caused by cancer, phantom limb pain, and cluster headaches. There are many more potential uses, but we will look at these in more detail as we move through the chapters.

For now, all you need to know is that Psilocybin, the compound in magic mushrooms, can have a deep impact on the brain, specifically in areas that regulate mood, awareness, and understanding. Many shroom users have stated that they feel more open-minded and relaxed after a magic mushroom encounter.

Magic mushrooms also can help us notice the good as well as the bad in ourselves and our environment, connecting us to nature on a whole other level. Many mushroom users also mention an increase in spirituality after consumption, stating they can feel how their ego just melts away. Some users even stated that during their trip they managed to see themselves and their personal troubles from a better, more positive perspective.

As mentioned previously, numerous research trials are being carried out to uncover more positive properties related to this jovial hallucinogen. So, the future of magic mushrooms is definitely an exhilarating one! Nobody knows what potential lies dormant in the humble shroom, but hopefully, loads of discoveries will be made in the next decade.

Shrooms just have a way of making the world way more interesting. Magic mushrooms can be some of the best tools we, as humans, have to alter the way we see, hear, and experience the world around us. If used responsibly, they can be amazing teachers. Something I bet you didn't know is that humans and shrooms have similar DNA structures! The mushroom's genetic composition is more related to humans than plants.

Take note though, it's imperative that you know exactly what you have before you even think about taking a bite!

If you consume a poisonous or toxic mushroom it can get very ugly.

This is where I come in. In this book, I'm going to take you by the hand and explain every step you need to take to ensure you forage and feast on only the best of the best!

Psilocybin helped me to slow down and come back to the present, which was a big thing for me. I used to be too immersed in the future, which can explain my feelings of anxiety back then. Others live in the past, more related to depression. Today, I feel honored to say that I truly enjoy the journey of life. And I believe Psilocybin was an important turning point.

During my experience, I was able to connect with others on a deeper, more spiritual level and it allowed me true introspection into my own life, experiencing beautiful sensations.

This guide is going to help you identify the good from the dangerous, show you how to grow them, and finally how to use them safely.

So, get ready to not just have your mind blown; be prepared to experience profound emotional revelations and a boost of creativity and positivity. Who knows, magic mushrooms might even provide you with that small nudge required to accelerate overall internal improvement, which could leave you feeling fulfilled and satisfied with just being.

Chapter 1: Shrooms Tell All Time

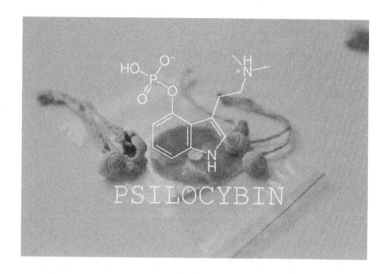

Nature alone is antique, and the oldest art a mushroom."-Thomas Carlyle

If you are curious about shrooms, their effects, the secret behind their magic, and their dangers, look no further! I'm going to give you the lowdown on these fantastical fungi! Before we go any further though, let me quickly explain what Psilocybin is. Not every mushroom has psychedelic effects, but the fungi that do contain this compound have been used for thousands of years.

Magic mushrooms can be broken down into two psychoactive ingredients, Psilocybin and Psilocin. Psilocybin, the primary psychoactive compound found in shrooms (which gives them their magical powers) is categorized as an indole-alkylamine. Psilocin is the compound primarily responsible for the euphoric effect also known as a "trip," working on the brain's serotonin receptors.

Psilocybin is rapidly metabolized (broken down) to Psilocin in the digestive tract once ingested. You must know that Psilocin degrades quickly in the exterior, making it a very unstable substance, even for laboratories, but because Psilocybin levels are much higher than Psilocin, the potency loss is so low that it's hardly noticeable, meaning the euphoric effect remains the same.

The hallucinatory properties of shrooms were originally discovered in the 1950s when a banker was invited by a native tribe to take part in their mushroom ritual during a healing ceremony in Mexico. He was so intrigued by these mini-wonders and their powers that he sent samples of the mushrooms to his friend, who just happened to be a Swiss chemist. The chemist managed to isolate the compound 'Psilocybin' from the mushrooms and created his own synthetic version 12 months later, known today as LSD (Lysergic acid diethylamide).

In the 70s, mushrooms started to get a bad rap and the federal government listed them under the most restricted group of drugs classified as Schedule 1, as they said shrooms have a "high potential for abuse" and could not be used for medicinal purposes because people would "misuse" them.

How They Work

Psilocybin is labeled a "classic psychedelic" because it can cause fluctuations in a person's mood, thought patterns, and awareness, as it imitates the neurotransmitters in the brain.

As you should know by now, once Psilocybin is ingested it gets broken down into Psilocin, which causes hallucinatory effects, including seeing images, hearing sounds, and feeling sensations that seem like reality even though it's all in the mind. Sometimes someone on Psilocybin can experience a mix of two senses, like smelling colors or seeing sound waves! No wonder people state that taking mushrooms can be a life-changing event.

Sensory augmentation, visual hallucinations, the feeling of becoming one with humanity as well as a sense of harmony are all effects that users mentioned they experienced while tripping.

It seems like Psilocybin has the potential to increase communication in specific areas of the brain that generally don't "speak" to one another, which could justify the new enhanced insight users experience under the effects of mushrooms...

Effects on the Brain

I think it's safe to say that we have established the fact that shrooms make you feel pretty good, but how do they affect the brain?

The National Institute on Drug Abuse stated that shrooms work similarly to any other hallucinogenic drug. They influence the neural pathways in the brain, closely resembling serotonin, a natural 'feel good' chemical the brain makes on its own. They mostly affect the prefrontal cortex, the area of the brain that controls your mood, abstract thinking, general perception, and your thought processes. The exact reason why Psilocybin triggers changes in your mood and your behavior is still a bit of a mystery, but scientists can say with certainty that the brain starts to communicate beyond its traditional programming when this compound is introduced to the system.

Before you get even more confused, I think it's time for a biology lesson! Your typical human brain has millions of neurons that are permanently firing while neurotransmitters travel a laid-out path from one area to the next. Some neural connections with a large load of "neural traffic" are programmed by the brain to become priority "highways," while other less busy connections are put on the back burner and only used when really necessary. Mushrooms take those less-used neuron pathways and allow them to travel to new destinations in the brain that are normally not accessible! Think of it as Psilocybin transforming a tiny dirt road into a newly paved main road. During this process, our thoughts are less focused on the outside world and our minds start to develop a new understanding of 'reality'. We leave our negative opinions behind while increasing our feelings of compassion and love towards the world and one another.

There is, of course, a very difficult scientific explanation for exactly what Psilocybin does to our brains, but in a nutshell, this compound could help us change our behavior. It actually increases our sense of openness, allowing us to break through our negative thought patterns, which could help with ailments such as depression, anxiety, and loads of other mental disorders!

Of course, more research will have to be done before we have a clear picture of the mind on mushrooms, but we will look at some existing research a bit later in this chapter!

Physical and Mental Effects

There is no "one size fits all" formula when it comes to the effects of shrooms on an individual. An estimate of 30 to 45 minutes is the general timeline to wait before feeling any Psilocybin effects on the body. It also depends on how you consumed it as well as if you ingested it on an empty stomach or not. Drinking a brew of shroom tea will have a quicker absorption rate than eating it, for example, and the exact species of shroom, plus the amount of hallucinogen in it, will play an important role in the physical effects you are going to feel.

It is recommended to take a smaller quantity rather than a larger dose if you are not sure of your shroom's powers. In fact, always start with a low dose if you are new to tripping just to be on the safe side. Don't stress too much about amounts right now; in the next chapter, I'll show you exactly how to measure the correct amounts using a dosage calculator.

The effects I have listed may vary from person to person, as it depends on the potency of the shroom, the amount you take, if the specimens are dry or fresh, how it has been prepared, and your sensitivity to the substance.

Physical Effects

If taken responsibly, you may not feel any of the effects at all, or barely a couple, but it is good to know them.

The physical effects you can expect to feel can include, but are not limited to:

- nausea that might lead to vomiting
- dilated pupils
- disorientation
- lack of coordination or exaggerated reflexes
- dry mouth
- heightened breathing and heart rate
- a rise in blood pressure
- increase in body temperature
- loss of appetite
- increased sweating
- sleep alterations
- headaches
- relaxation

Tolerance to shrooms can build up quickly, so it's suggested that you have a resting period after your first dose. This means that an individual may need to increase the dose to experience the same hallucinogenic effect. Take note: Those who take large doses of Psilocybin can have a super intense experience of paranoia, sheer panic, and scary hallucinations. During an overdose, users might fall into a psychosis where they are completely detached from reality, called an "Ego Death." Abusing mushrooms can cause a toxic shock or even death if a lethal mushroom has been ingested. If you experience severe vomiting, stomach aches, and diarrhea after you have consumed mushrooms, you might have been poisoned and should go to an emergency unit immediately.

Mental Effects

As mentioned before, Psilocybin is well-known for its intense alteration of your emotional awareness and your psychological understanding. The neuroscience of Psilocybin is still in its infancy stage, but what we do know is that people experience hallucinations, auditory enhancement, and heightened emotional enlightenment, as Psilocybin works on the serotonin system of the mind.

Intensity levels will determine what you feel and how, depending on the dosage, person, etc., which we will cover in some of the following chapters. But for now, you can expect:

- sensory augmentation
- time standing still or fleeting past quickly
- objects seem to be shifting and changing
- patterns and shapes noticed on walls
- extraordinary thoughts
- personal understanding and reflection on self
- happy feelings
- euphoria
- synaesthesia

- introspective (spiritual) experiences
- bright colors
- panic or paranoia
- intensified feelings

Your mindset will have a massive impact on your mental state during a mushroom trip. Try to avoid large crowds, negative people, and intense surroundings like busy streets or heavy city lighting.

Because people are different, each experience will have a different outcome. There is a possibility that your first trip or any other trip could become slightly intense, or even a bit overwhelming at times. An excellent tip is to move away from noise and stimulation. Also remind yourself that you took a substance that will just last temporarily, breathe and try to relax. Go with the flow and do what you feel attracted to. Accept your experience without fighting it – literally!

Risks

As with any mind- or mood-altering substance, there are risks involved and shrooms are no different. The most common adverse side effects of magic mushrooms include a so-called bad trip, which could involve physical symptoms like nausea, vomiting, headaches, and icy chills. As a bad trip has more to do with the mind, I'll give you a quick summary of what symptoms might occur. You will not know that you are going to have a bad trip until you are smack-bang in the middle of one, so it's good to know what to expect.

Unpleasant physical sensations, hallucinations, and negative thoughts are some of the things 'shroomies' could experience during a bad trip. Some people have said it felt as if time stood still and they were stuck in a moment, almost like in the movie, Groundhog Day... Other users have mentioned that they started feeling paranoid, distrusting the people they previously had no issues with. Typical negative hallucinations during a bad trip include walls breathing, friends' faces becoming distorted or changing into scary monsters as well as seeing objects that aren't really there. Negative mood swings might also occur, but you need to remember you are on a trip, all these things will disappear as soon as the effects of the shrooms wear off.

Please, be aware of all this, but don't let this information scare you either. If you take the recommended dose responsibly, chances are you won't have any of these experiences! For those who took a bit too much and are uncomfortable with their trip, taking lavender or valerian root can help to ease the anxiety. Consuming it will speed up the process. If you fear that you need medical attention, you might have to visit the emergency room at your local hospital.

There are many Psychonauts out there who can suggest their own remedies for the alleviation of a bad trip like citric acid or a good over-the-counter (OTC) sedative. My advice is to steer clear of any so-called quick fixes.

It's definitely not a good idea to throw more ingredients into an already volatile situation; you never know what medicines could have a bad reaction when mixed! The consequences could be extremely negative.

Some users have reported visual flashbacks. Not every user has a negative experience, but generally, flashbacks don't have the best reputation. Negative flashbacks can occur days or weeks after a trip on shrooms but can also be months or even years after initial ingestion. The experience typically varies.

There is the risk of a rare paralysis (wood lover paralysis), which shouldn't be underestimated, it seems to come only from mushrooms that grow on wood, hence the name. Symptoms appear hours after ingestion and include weakness, lack of coordination, or even paralysis.

Others mentioned a heightened feeling of distress, confusion, anxiety, and in extreme cases, the onset of psychosis after ingesting large quantities of mushrooms. These symptoms usually disappear after a few hours or once the effects of Psilocybin begin to wear off.

Mushrooms are not physically addictive and there are no withdrawal symptoms attached after stopping use, but some people might experience psychological withdrawal and struggle to adjust to their reality after abusing them.

Psilocybin can aggravate or trigger dormant psychotic disorders, so if you have a history of mental conditions in the family, including schizophrenia, it's best to steer clear from shrooms altogether.

Last, but not least, continuing the use of Psilocybin could increase your risk of cardiovascular disorders, but if you stick to microdoses and sporadic use you should be safe. I personally prefer using low doses as they produce the greatest therapeutic benefits and I like the idea of being relatively in control. My girlfriend has opted for microdoses and uses low doses on special occasions. During my interviews with friends, some have mentioned using higher doses throwing themselves into the world of "Jumanji" where anything can happen. They all made sure there was a friend to supervise, I must add.

Research, Potential Therapy, and More!

Imagine a room-dimly lit, soft tranquil music playing in the background, funky art deco walls, and one very comfortable couch. No, I'm not talking about a cool living room from the 1960s! I'm essentially describing an area in a modern research facility.

Joe is undergoing a Psilocybin session. He has earphones and dark shades on, while a research team is busy guiding him through his trip on shrooms. He is not bouncing off the walls, not babbling any nonsense either; he is actually experiencing a high level of introspection. Mushrooms are still illegal in most of the world, so there is a medical unit on site just in case this therapy session goes south, but make no mistake, the power of Psilocybin is beginning to be unearthed!

In recent years, many trials have started to pop up and research has proven that magic mushrooms could potentially treat a variety of psychiatric illnesses and behavioral conditions. None of these clinical tests have been approved by the FDA yet, so we can't say with certainty that Psilocybin is the new cure-all drug, but it does have many medicinal benefits!

Scientists have mentioned that magic mushrooms could uplift people who suffer from depression, help those struggling with obsessive-compulsive disorders, assist in various addictions, and even alleviate headaches as well as other cancer-related ailments.

Even though there are numerous initiatives out there trying to decriminalize magic mushrooms, many medical experts fear that these laws will not be lifted any time soon, unfortunately.

At the moment Psilocybin mushrooms are still deemed as a Schedule I drug, but regardless of all the legal "red tape" researchers have begun reshaping the negative stigma linked to shrooms with new clinical trials ready for FDA approval.

Two main areas of Psilocybin research currently ongoing include fighting addiction as well as helping to decrease cancer-related psychiatric disorders. Studies vary and could be as small as one individual pilot program or as large as an entire institute focusing on

Psilocybin uses and benefits. Here's what the current research says about Psilocybin treatment:

Depression

Researchers have suggested that Psilocybin could relieve major depression in sufferers for as long as 12 months because of the psychedelic compound "opening up" a depressed person's brain making their negative thinking patterns more pliable and susceptible to change.

The findings, after trials, revealed that Psilocybin transforms the brain, making its circuitry more flexible and the mind more supple, changing rigid and restricted neural pathways that can help the mind break out of its negative frame of thinking.

The difference between magic mushrooms and other antidepressants is that the positive effects of Psilocybin can be traced a few months after consumption, making it a powerful alternative to medications that have to be taken on a daily basis.

Compared to general antidepressants, Psilocybin relieves symptoms of depression with only one or two treatments, so patients will not have to rely on pills or tablets taken regularly.

More studies will need to be done, but this is groundbreaking research that could change millions of lives!

Stopping Smoking and Terminating Addiction

Magic mushrooms have become a promising treatment option for patients who want to break their dependence on illegal substances, such as cocaine and opioids. A professor of psychiatry at a university in New York reported that abstinence was quite high among addicts after they used Psilocybin and studies showed a decline in the use of many illegal substances as well as cigarettes for up to a year. Johns Hopkins University carried out an experiment where professional staff administered a high dose of Psilocybin to alcohol abusers on two separate occasions in a closely controlled environment. Reports revealed that these two single doses were enough to help folks with alcohol dependency overcome their addiction.

In theory, Psilocybin can break a substance user's routine, offering them a glimpse into the "bigger picture" of life, and allowing them to step outside their issues and into a new vantage point.

Pain

According to the National Library of Medicine, there is clinical evidence that shows the potential benefit of Psilocybin mushrooms in decreasing cancer pain and phantom limb pain.

An experimental breakthrough in a condition known as cluster headache has changed the lives of those who struggle with this terrible ailment. Those who have experienced these types of headaches are aware of their debilitating effects on the brain. Many cluster headache sufferers commit suicide because they can't live with the pain. Sufferers can have from one to ten cluster headache attacks a day. Magic mushrooms have proven to help many sufferers who use microdoses of a compound categorized as 5meO-DALT. Almost every sufferer who has found relief from their headaches has said that shrooms gave them their life back.

Migraine is another lingering headache disorder that impacts many people's lives who have to shell out thousands of dollars a year in medical costs as well as having to live with a major loss of productivity in their work.

Many treatment practices for headache disorders show insufficient effectiveness as sufferers begin to build up a tolerance to the medication or feel no relief from the medicines they take. Migraines can be so intense and disabling that patients resort to other types of experimental remedies that can be dangerous and illegal. The great news is that in prior studies, it has been recorded that Psilocybin given in microdoses not only can assist with lessening the pain but also eliminate the headaches completely.

None of the patients treated with Psilocybin complained of any harmful effects and had no withdrawal symptoms after the discontinuation of their treatment.

Scientists say that the full potential of shrooms as a medical alternative to usual migraine medicines will still have to be explored, but from the reports in past studies, it is clear that they could be tremendously beneficial to extreme headache sufferers.

Another trial from Johns Hopkins in 2016 reported that one dose of Psilocybin actually improved the quality of life in cancer patients and reduced depression as well as anxiety in people who suffer from HIV and Aids.

Brain Boosters

Studies have shown that Psilocybin boosts neurogenesis—the growth of new brain cells (neurons). This can help a person overcome extreme feelings of distress, and it may be a contributing factor to learning and memory.

More studies will need to be done, but following this approach, it is said that Psilocybin could reduce the effects of hazardous stimuli that harm brain cells, or even reverse depression, improving this natural process in a specific area of the brain called the hippocampus.

Eating Disorders

The medical health field has begun investigating the possible benefits of using Psilocybin-assisted therapy to treat eating disorders. Psilocybin has the ability to rewire one's brain, potentially focusing on the root cause of eating disorders instead of just treating the symptoms.

The precise processes in the brain are not fully understood yet, but in theory, Psilocybin reduces or breaks down the default mode network (DMN). This network has established communication pathways between the different brain regions, sometimes creating certain misfit patterns; for example, eating without hunger or skipping meals. Over time, it becomes challenging to create new patterns, so we will stick to the established ones.

The default mode network seems to be overactive in certain mental health conditions, including eating disorders, and people can struggle with reasoning. Psilocybin could allow the brain to form new mental tracks by breaking those old patterns, providing the opportunity for the person to detect the true nature of these patterns and realize that, just like many social fears, these patterns are intended to help you, but are not adapted to reality, changing a person's point of view entirely.

Relationship Savers

Here you are, sitting in a waiting room, paging through an old magazine wondering how you ended up in couples' therapy.

You love your partner and you are pretty sure they love you. So, since when did your love turn into a thought, instead of a feeling? When did it become a distant memory? You want to go back to the days when you both felt that sense of true intimacy. You are tired of talking in circles where words mean nothing anymore...

Does any of this sound familiar? Many of us wish we could just take a pill or a so-called "love drug" to enhance our relationships and jump-start that fire in our guts again, bringing back that enchanted arousal when our partner looks at us in a certain way.

We know there is no fix-it-all tablet and no love potion that can magically solve our relationship woes, but what if I told you that many couples are turning to Psilocybin as the answer to their love troubles?

Magic mushrooms have the ability to provide our brains with that extra "shove" to curb our inhibitions and change the way we perceive love and attachment. This is why it comes as no surprise that couples have been experimenting with shrooms together, either to build stronger, more profound bonds or to deal with some deep-rooted issues. Many couples just use shrooms to share and enjoy their euphoric experiences together. Regardless of the reason, shrooms can produce a deep sense of connection and boundlessness, which means that if you trip together the sense of self-transformation becomes a dual transformation that you both experience.

Tripping with your lover is different from tripping with friends because there's that deeper connection between the two of you. There is a heightened sense of belonging and an unmatched connection where your souls start to intertwine, and you can physically feel the strands of energy tying you together again.

Tripping together can have a major positive impact on your love connection and physical intimacy taking your relationship to the next level. As you become more comfortable tripping with your partner, it becomes easier to share your deepest, darkest fantasies with them.

This might sound very daunting to many people who struggle to have those difficult conversations with their other half. Instead of trying to control the situation, you can begin to face your issues together and start realizing how grateful you should be for each other. You could even realize your relationship is all but doomed as you begin to communicate about how you can work on fixing your situation. Tripping on shrooms might bring you closer together than any couples counselor or therapist could. If used correctly mushrooms might be a helpful love drug.

I'm not saying that traditional couples counseling is bad, and you need to understand that regular, everyday relationship complications can be addressed successfully through talk therapy. The point of tripping together is not to "fix what is broken" but to work on improving your relationship, from whatever baseline you happen to be as a couple.

Shroomy Summary

Wow! I have given you a truckload of information, but I'm going to leave you with a short summary of 'shroomy' facts and important information to jolt your memory just in case you don't have time to read through all the pages again.

- Psilocybin is the main compound in shrooms that give them their psychedelic effect.

- Psilocybin breaks down into Psilocin once in the body.

- Users can experience sensory augmentation as well as visual hallucinations when using mushrooms.

- Psilocybin and Psilocin mimic the neurotransmitters in the brain, causing an overall feeling of well-being during your trip.

- An average waiting period of 30 to 45 minutes is expected before the effects start to kick in.

- Once ingested, you can expect a feeling of euphoria for approximately three hours, but a trip could last as long as six hours.

- If you have zero experience with magic mushrooms, start with lower doses to ensure a nice, safe, and enjoyable trip.

- Stick to microdoses if you want to use shrooms for therapeutic treatments without any physical or mental "high" effect.

- The intensity of the effects will depend on the Psilocybin quantity, metabolization time, and your sensitivity to the active component.

- Psilocybin tolerance builds and dissipates quickly, so rest for one to two weeks between trips, and one to two days when microdosing.

- Physical, mental, and emotional effects could include nausea, yawning (initial effect), dilated pupils, relaxation, loss of appetite, sensory augmentation, visual effects or hallucinations, euphoria, headache, heightened thought processes and introspection, increased heart rate, etc. Other negative physical feelings might include some discomfort, paranoia, anxiety, or fear.

- If your trip feels too intense, try to remind yourself that the effects will start to diminish as the mushrooms' effects begin to wear off.

- Do not use mushrooms if you know that you have a family history of psychotic disorders or mental conditions, as mushrooms can aggravate these ailments.

- Remember to just go with the flow, relax and enjoy wherever your 'shroomy' experience takes you!

I hope you are becoming as excited about mushrooms, their benefits, and their potential healing properties as I am because I still have much to share with you! Now that we have covered the basics, I think it's time to move on to the next chapter.

If you are enjoying this book so far, it would mean a lot to me if you could take a minute to review or rate it on the respective platform you acquired it from. Did you know that just 0.5 - 1% of readers do actually end up leaving a review? I have to admit that I used to not be that 1%, but now I do it different since I know how meaningful this can be to independent writers.

Chapter 2: No More Dosing Dilemmas

Right, you managed to secure your first bag of shrooms and while you are looking at these stunning little delicacies, you are wondering how much is too much or too little?

When dealing with shroom doses you can't play Goldilocks trying each bear's bowl of porridge until you find the one that is just right.

Shroom doses can be a little bit tricky, especially if you consider the fact that there are more than 180 different varieties and potency levels out there.

Before moving to the next section, I would like to mention you can find low-cost kits that accurately measure potency levels.

Measuring Strength Properly

The strength of any psychedelic mushroom is measured by the amount of Psilocybin it contains as well as its levels of Psilocin. The sum of these two components makes up the potency profile of your shroom.

It's recommended to know the species of mushroom as well as its potency levels, so you know exactly what you are working with.

You will also have to keep in mind what you want from your shroom experience and your reasons for taking them. Do you want to use them for their medicinal properties? Do you want a light trip or a full-blown magic mushroom extravaganza?

Before we go into deeper detail, let's investigate the different kinds of mushroom doses.

Microdosing

When you use microdoses, you are basically taking such a small amount of mushrooms that you probably won't even feel any psychedelic effects. A microdose is also known as a sub-perceptual dose, which means the user won't experience much change in their visual perception and won't trip. Microdoses are used when individuals want to enhance their creativity, increase their energy levels, elevate their mood, focus more or allow for deeper internalizing and profound thinking patterns, but you can generally just carry on with your daily life as normal.

The dose is normally below 0.25 grams but can also be below 0.5 grams depending on the person, among other factors. Before you try to work out exactly how many grams you will need, relax, we are going to study dosage levels and measurements in a minute. At the moment, I just want to explain the kinds of doses and what you can expect when taking each one.

Low Mushroom Dose

Low shroom doses allow you to feel some psychedelic effects but are still not enough to let you trip out completely. There is no exact measurement to ensure you use a low dose compared to a microdose, but some reactions to expect when on a low dose include a slight physical high, enhanced senses, bright colors, deeper thoughts, a fuzzy feeling of euphoria, and a tiny bit of light-headedness. You will have the impression that something is scratching the appearance and sensation of reality and even the music will sound better.

A typical low dose of magic mushrooms is generally ½ gram up to 1 gram (dry). Many people use low doses to enhance their senses as well as to 'test the waters' when just starting to experiment with shrooms. With a low dose, your chances of staying in control are much better than at higher doses. Some users might become anxious on low doses while waiting for psychedelic effects, which never arrive. Thus, stick to advised doses if you are looking for a specific outcome.

Moderate Mushroom Dose

Now, we are starting to move towards heavier psychedelic effects and shroom users will have a more intense trip. On moderate doses colors will be even brighter, you can start seeing objects moving or morphing into something else, walls will have beautiful patterns, and everything just feels better! Emotional response to music will be higher, people and things may be funnier now, your senses much more heightened with possible synaesthesia, tactile experiences will increase, and time might feel as if it's slowing down or speeding up. A moderate dose starts at 1 gram and can move up to 3 grams.

High Mushroom Dose

When you move to high doses of magic mushrooms you are now playing in the big leagues. This is where your trip becomes incredibly intense, and everything can seem distorted. You can expect massive changes to your thought patterns, visual perception, and mood. Hallucinations are almost guaranteed both visually and auditory. Your trip might feel like you are in a dream state. You might see visions or have a feeling of dissociation from your body, or even experience the presence of a divine entity! 'Ego Death' might also occur in this phase. A high dose of magic mushrooms can vary from 3 to 5 grams.

The 'Heroic Dose'

This dose is not called heroic for no reason. When you ingest these quantities of shrooms you go beyond your average trip filled with flowers, rainbows, and giggles.

This dose is a powerful one for users who want to abandon their physical bodies to become one with the universe, find answers to hidden questions, and even communicate with entities not seen in our world! None of the other doses described beforehand comes close to the heroic dose's potency or magical tripping powers. Ingesting such a high amount of shrooms makes it tough to explain exactly what you'll experience or go through. 'Ego Death' or dissolution is common at this enhanced level where you leave behind your consciousness and see things from a spiritual viewpoint. The heroic dose starts at four grams, but many users have mentioned even higher amounts.

Do not even try a heroic dose if you don't have someone with you. Most people go "heroic" during mushroom ceremonies or retreats.

Take note: These are not dosing guidelines. Doses will never be precise, due to many factors like species, preservation, etc. These are general dosage amounts. I merely tried to give you a tiny peek into the various doses and what you could expect from each. (Going from zero to an overly intense trip.)

Typical Magic Mushroom Doses:

- Microdose: 0.1–0.5 grams.

- Low Dose: 0.5–1 gram.

- Moderate Dose: 1–3 grams.

- High Dose: 3–5 grams and above.

Typical Psilocybin Doses:

- Microdose: < 4 mg.

- Low dose: 4–8 mg.

- Average dose: 6–20 mg.

- High dose: 20–35 mg.

Remember, increasing the dose means that the trip's intensity levels are going to rise as well, affecting the duration itself. An average trip starts after 45 minutes, the most intense effects or reaching your peak will roughly occur within the first two hours, typically 90 minutes from ingestion, thereafter, you may start to descend, and the world will begin returning to normal.

Dosage Guide

Thanks to technology you do not have to sit with a pen and paper to figure out exactly what dose you can handle.

The main aspects to consider when calculating the correct dosage for your physique include your body weight, the type of mushroom species or truffles, and the method of ingestion; dried or raw.

Body weight being a factor is controversial because sensitivity to Psilocybin varies from person to person, a rough calculation of body weights can be found below for the two main mushroom species known as Cubensis and Panaeolus cyanescens, as well as Magic Truffles:

Body Weight 40 Kg	MOI	Microdose	Low Dose	Normal Dose	High Dose
CUBENSIS	Fresh	1.2 GRAMS	5.0 GRAMS	12.0 GRAMS	18.0 GRAMS
PANAEOLUS CYANESCENS	Fresh	0.2 GRAMS	1.0 GRAMS	2.4 GRAMS	3.6 GRAMS
CUBENSIS	Dry	0.1 GRAMS	0.5 GRAMS	1.2 GRAMS	1.8 GRAMS
PANAEOLUS CYANESCENS	Dry	0.02 GRAMS	0.1 GRAMS	0.2 GRAMS	0.4 GRAMS
TRUFFLES	Fresh	0.5 GRAMS	3.8 GRAMS	5.2 GRAMS	8.8 GRAMS
TRUFFLES	Dry	0.3 GRAMS	2.5 GRAMS	3.4 GRAMS	5.7 GRAMS

Body Weight 50 Kg	MOI	Microdose	Low Dose	Normal Dose	High Dose
CUBENSIS	Fresh	1.5 GRAMS	6.3 GRAMS	15.0 GRAMS	22.5 GRAMS
PANAEOLUS CYANESCENS	Fresh	0.3 GRAMS	1.3 GRAMS	3.0 GRAMS	4.5 GRAMS
CUBENSIS	Dry	0.1 GRAMS	0.6 GRAMS	1.5 GRAMS	2.3 GRAMS
PANAEOLUS CYANESCENS	Dry	0.03 Grams	0.1 GRAMS	0.3 GRAMS	0.5 GRAMS
TRUFFLES	Fresh	0.7 GRAMS	4.7 GRAMS	6.5 GRAMS	11.0 GRAMS
TRUFFLES	Dry	0.4 GRAMS	3.1 GRAMS	4.2 GRAMS	7.1 GRAMS

Body Weight 60 Kg	MOI	Microdose	Low Dose	Normal Dose	High Dose
CUBENSIS	Fresh	1.8 GRAMS	7.5 GRAMS	18.0 GRAMS	27.0 GRAMS
PANAEOLUS CYANESCENS	Fresh	0.4 GRAMS	1.5 GRAMS	3.6 GRAMS	5.4 GRAMS
CUBENSIS	Dry	0.2 GRAMS	0.8 GRAMS	1.8 GRAMS	2.7 GRAMS
PANAEOLUS CYANESCENS	Dry	0.04 GRAMS	0.1 GRAMS	0.4 GRAMS	0.5 GRAMS
TRUFFLES	Fresh	0.8 GRAMS	5.6 GRAMS	7.8 GRAMS	13.2 GRAMS
TRUFFLES	Dry	0.5 GRAMS	3.7 GRAMS	5.0 GRAMS	8.6 GRAMS

Body Weight 70 Kg	MOI	Microdose	Low Dose	Normal Dose	High Dose
CUBENSIS	Fresh	3.1 GRAMS	8.8 GRAMS	21.0 GRAMS	31.5 GRAMS
PANAEOLUS CYANESCENS	Fresh	0.6 GRAMS	1.8 GRAMS	4.2 GRAMS	6.3 GRAMS
CUBENSIS	Dry	0.2 GRAMS	0.9 GRAMS	2.1 GRAMS	3.1 GRAMS
PANAEOLUS CYANESCENS	Dry	0.04 GRAMS	0.2 GRAMS	0.4 GRAMS	0.6 GRAMS
TRUFFLES	Fresh	0.9 GRAMS	6.6 GRAMS	9.1 GRAMS	15.4 GRAMS
TRUFFLES	Dry	0.6 GRAMS	4.3 GRAMS	5.9 GRAMS	10.0 GRAMS

Body Weight 80 Kg	MOI	Microdose	Low Dose	Normal Dose	High Dose
CUBENSIS	Fresh	2.4 GRAMS	10.0 GRAMS	24.0 GRAMS	36.0 GRAMS
PANAEOLUS CYANESCENS	Fresh	0.5 GRAMS	2.0 GRAMS	4.8 GRAMS	7.2 GRAMS
CUBENSIS	Dry	0.2 GRAMS	1.0 GRAMS	2.4 GRAMS	3.6 GRAMS
PANAEOLUS CYANESCENS	Dry	0.05 GRAMS	0.2 GRAMS	0.5 GRAMS	0.7 GRAMS
TRUFFLES	Fresh	1.0 GRAMS	7.5 GRAMS	10.4 GRAMS	17.6 GRAMS
TRUFFLES	Dry	0.7 GRAMS	5.0 GRAMS	6.7 GRAMS	11.4 GRAMS

Body Weight 90 Kg	MOI	Microdose	Low Dose	Normal Dose	High Dose
CUBENSIS	Fresh	2.7 GRAMS	11.3 GRAMS	27.0 GRAMS	40.5 GRAMS
PANAEOLUS CYANESCENS	Fresh	0.5 GRAMS	2.3 GRAMS	5.4 GRAMS	8.1 GRAMS
CUBENSIS	Dry	0.3 GRAMS	1.1 GRAMS	2.7 GRAMS	4.0 GRAMS
PANAEOLUS CYANESCENS	Dry	0.1 GRAMS	0.2 GRAMS	0.5 GRAMS	0.8 GRAMS
TRUFFLES	Fresh	1.2 GRAMS	8.5 GRAMS	11.7 GRAMS	19.8 GRAMS
TRUFFLES	Dry	0.8 GRAMS	5.6 GRAMS	7.6 GRAMS	12.9 GRAMS

Body Weight 100 Kg	MOI	Microdose	Low Dose	Normal Dose	High Dose
CUBENSIS	Fresh	3.0 GRAMS	12.5 GRAMS	30.0 GRAMS	45.0 GRAMS
PANAEOLUS CYANESCENS	Fresh	0.6 GRAMS	2.5 GRAMS	6.0 GRAMS	9.0 GRAMS
CUBENSIS	Dry	0.3 GRAMS	1.3 GRAMS	3.0 GRAMS	4.5 GRAMS
PANAEOLUS CYANESCENS	Dry	0.1 GRAMS	0.3 GRAMS	0.6 GRAMS	0.9 GRAMS
TRUFFLES	Fresh	1.3 GRAMS	9.4 GRAMS	13.0 GRAMS	22.0 GRAMS
TRUFFLES	Dry	0.8 GRAMS	6.2 GRAMS	8.4 GRAMS	14.3 GRAMS

Body Weight 120 Kg	MOI	Microdose	Low Dose	Normal Dose	High Dose
CUBENSIS	Fresh	3.6 GRAMS	15.0 GRAMS	36.0 GRAMS	54.0 GRAMS
PANAEOLUS CYANESCENS	Fresh	0.7 GRAMS	3.0 GRAMS	7.2 GRAMS	10.8 GRAMS
CUBENSIS	Dry	0.4 GRAMS	1.5 GRAMS	3.6 GRAMS	5.4 GRAMS
PANAEOLUS CYANESCENS	Dry	0.1 GRAMS	0.3 GRAMS	0.7 GRAMS	1.1 GRAMS
TRUFFLES	Fresh	1.6 GRAMS	11.3 GRAMS	15.6 GRAMS	26.4 GRAMS
TRUFFLES	Dry	1.0 GRAMS	7.4 GRAMS	10.1 GRAMS	17.2 GRAMS

Body Weight 140 Kg	MOI	Microdose	Low Dose	Normal Dose	High Dose
CUBENSIS	Fresh	4.2 GRAMS	17.5 GRAMS	42.0 GRAMS	63.0 GRAMS
PANAEOLUS CYANESCENS	Fresh	0.8 GRAMS	3.5 GRAMS	8.4 GRAMS	12.6 GRAMS
CUBENSIS	Dry	0.4 GRAMS	1.8 GRAMS	4.2 GRAMS	6.3 GRAMS
PANAEOLUS CYANESCENS	Dry	0.1 GRAMS	0.3 GRAMS	0.8 GRAMS	1.3 GRAMS
TRUFFLES	Fresh	1.8 GRAMS	13.2 GRAMS	18.2 GRAMS	30.8 GRAMS
TRUFFLES	Dry	1.2 GRAMS	8.7 GRAMS	11.8 GRAMS	20.0 GRAMS

Note that the Panaeolus cyanescens is 4 times stronger when dried and 5 times stronger when fresh. If you noticed that the calculation is not proportional, it's because the Psilocin to Psilocybin ratio (when fresh) is much higher than the Psilocybe cubensis ratio. Remember, as soon as the Psilocin is exposed to oxygen and heat, it begins to degrade.

Doses among different strains should never be taken for granted, though, and users have to bear in mind that the concentration variations among them are not always proportional. It's vital to know the shroom's Psilocin to Psilocybin ratio, before taking any size dose.

Classic Consumables

How can you take Psilocybin mushrooms? What is the best way to make sure they keep most of their magic and pack a booming punch?

It's said that for higher effectiveness it's generally better to eat the mushrooms without adding anything, on an empty stomach, with no heat exposure. This is the classic way, but I will still walk you through a few different methods so you can have several options to choose from.

Step One: Clean Those Babies!

If you have decided to give it a go and eat them raw, the most important tip I can give you is to clean them properly! Most shrooms that are grown in controlled environments are probably not covered in manure, but if you went on a shroom hunt in the forest, chances are you have no idea what they have been growing in, so assume the worst and do your best to brush them dry leaving them gleaming and shiny.

Cleaning mushrooms is pretty easy. Just make sure you wipe off any visible dirt and do not use water, it is not recommended.

You can use a dry, clean brush with stiff, hard bristles to wipe off most of the soil and dirt or wipe them clean with a moist paper towel.

As soon as they are dry you can give it a go and start chomping on them but keep at hand a cool drink or juice, or something tasty like chocolate if you can't handle their taste.

A smoothie could be one of the simplest ways to ingest your shrooms. All you have to do is crush your mushrooms until they become a powdery consistency and then start adding fruit or vegetables into your blender, combining everything until you are happy with your mix. Measure out the correct amount of shrooms to add to your smoothie so you don't end up with a heroic dose by mistake!

Mix with Other Food

This approach has so many ways and methods. You can sprinkle your dried shrooms on anything and everything! Just keep in mind that they are sensitive to heat, so if you want them to keep their original potency, keep them cool. Mix them into pasta, use them as a spread on crackers, or mix them into your peanut butter for your breakfast toast, your imagination is your only limit, so go crazy and try to find as many ways as possible to mix your shrooms into your food!

Infused Baking

What about putting tiny bits of shrooms into ice cream, chocolate bars, brownies, or cookies? Break or crumble your shrooms and add them to any mixture as soon as it cools down. Psilocybin starts to break down at high temperatures, being 343°F/172°C the melting point for Psilocin, and 427°F/220°C for Psilocybin. The Psilocin melting point is measured on Methanol, and the oxygen molecules contained in the water would break down this substance.

Tea

After eating them raw, drinking shroom tea is the second-best way to keep your shrooms' strength during consumption without compromising potency levels. Making tea is one of the best methods to avoid nausea as we only use the bits of the shrooms we want to infuse our brew while discarding the rest.

One cup of tea will include one gram of shrooms, but you can adapt the recipe to your preferred dose. Boil the water, add your preference of tea mix, and allow it to cool down a little bit before adding your shrooms, the smaller the pieces the better. Leave your brew for 10-15 minutes to allow the shrooms time to infuse and stir it occasionally. Feel free to add some honey. And as soon as all the shrooms have settled at the bottom of your cup you can sit back, relax and sip away while watching your world turn into a wonderland!

There is no real evidence at the time this book is being written that suggests Psilocybin degrades at 212°F/100 °C. We just know that Psilocybin is sensitive to heat, and we will try to avoid unnecessarily high temperatures. Also, don't forget that some shrooms taste worse than others, so avoid cooking with the ones that will just infuse the rest of your food with their nasty flavors!

Lemon Tek

Psilocybin converts to Psilocin when exposed to the acid of fresh lemon juice. Lemon Tek is a process where you use ground-up shrooms and lemon or lime juice to create a natural drink. The effects will kick in faster, and the trip will be more intense, but it won't last as long as a regular one.

So again, cut the shrooms into small pieces and mix them with the juice allowing the shrooms to rest for 15 to 30 minutes before drinking it. You've just uncovered a new way to further enhance your shroomy experience!

Gel Capsules

This approach is for the more experienced shroom user. When your shrooms are dry you can finely grind them and fill empty gel capsules with your shroom dust. Gel capsules keep the shrooms intact if you are planning on storing them for later, and if you have a scale, you can work out your dosages too. Again, grind your shrooms up until they become a fine powder, and fill the empty capsules using a capsule machine.

Magical Munchies

Whether you prefer them fresh or dehydrated, broken up or ground into a powder, magic mushrooms can be taken on such a wide spectrum, which makes it easy to disguise their somewhat bitter taste. As I said before, you can do whatever you like to make consuming your shrooms easier and tastier. If you are not the type of person that is satisfied with sprinkling dry, raw shrooms on bland foods or making weak tasteless tea you can try your skills at creating amazing shroomy delights...

A reminder for beginner shroomies—it's best to stick to small doses and start slowly. You can always add more to your dish or your brew, but if you go overboard and add too much, you will have to ride that shroom wave all the way to the end!

Mushrooms Versus Truffles

At first, you might think truffles and mushrooms are completely different species because they don't look similar at all. The truth is that they actually belong to the same organism. Let me first say this, magic truffles are not the truffles most people see on the menu in a fancy restaurant. When I speak of magic truffles, I'm referring to a species called Sclerotia, which typically grows underground. Magic truffles species include Psilocybe mexicana, Psilocybe atlantis, Psilocybe tampanensis, and Psilocybe galindoi.

Magic truffles are like a food source for their mushroom family growing above the soil and most shrooms have Sclerotia or truffles buried beneath them.

Now that you have distinguished the fact that both magic mushrooms and magic truffles belong to the same organism, it might be easier to understand why the two are often compared. There are some noticeable differences, though. The first is the most obvious: One grows above ground while the other prefers the darkness of the underground world. The second distinct difference is their appearance. Shrooms are soft with a fine structure, while truffles are darker and much rougher.

Normally mushrooms start growing underground, but eventually they rise to the surface as they grow to release their spores and eventually finish their cycle of life. Magic truffles stay underground throughout their lifespan and are actually a type of survival strategy mushrooms have developed when struggling to grow. When conditions aren't favorable, the mushroom will grow Sclerotia as a food source just in case something threatens its existence. If the mushroom cannot thrive in its environment and its fruiting body dies, these durable forms of concentrated mycelium (a compound in truffles) can live dormant for many years waiting for the right time to regrow and 'mushroom'.

The magic mushroom's purpose is to reproduce, they are programmed that way. Magic truffles are designed to self-preserve, but both serve the same function as both contain Psilocybin. Some mushroom users say truffles are not as potent as their shroomy cousins and that their trip is a bit weaker, but in many cases, their psychedelic effects are extremely similar. Truffles with a lower potency mean that consumers will have to ingest larger dosages. It is important to mention that the potency of each truffle species varies, so make sure you know how high the levels of Psilocybin are before you take a larger dose than necessary.

Some shroom users state that magic mushroom trips have more visual effects than magic truffles, but as we know by now, Psilocybin does the same thing regardless of the jacket it wears. Mushrooms have different potencies because none of them are the same size, weight, or height. Truffles are denser and more compact, meaning that each truffle in the mycelium cake will have almost the same amount of Psilocybin.

The way you grow these two cousins differ and there are also differences when harvesting them. Magic mushrooms can be picked after they have matured, whereas magic truffles grow underground and have to be dug up after the shroom has been harvested. Both truffles and shrooms are dried, although truffles have a much lower amount of moisture inside them. They take less time to dry, but the process for drying and storing them is almost identical.

You can buy magic truffles online and they will be mailed straight to you! They even come with instructions and are ready to eat! Unfortunately, you won't find any shrooms online, you can buy spores and grow kits, though, so if you're up to the challenge, try to cultivate your own!

Without going into too much boring detail, you can expect to get a similar experience from consuming a magic mushroom and a magic truffle if they came from the exact same species.

Caps or Stems?

Let's end this chapter with one last question: Which is more potent—caps or stalks? If you have the time and enough shrooms, it seems like the caps have more psychoactive content, but honestly, the difference is so minute that I wouldn't bother separating the two. In the end, I would say it would be a waste to throw away the stalks and I've learned that you must never underestimate any part of these supernaturally splendid fungi!

Shroomy Summary

Let's look at some of the key takeaways in this chapter:

- There are various dosage amounts and each dose has a variety of effects. When deciding on a dose of shrooms, first decide what you would like the ultimate outcome to be.

- A microdose is a very small dose of mushrooms that is not enough to generate a "trip" or any kind of hallucination, but it is believed that this amount can produce a variety of positive health benefits.

- A low dose of mushrooms will begin to give you some psychedelic effects, but not enough to be regarded as a full-blown trip. It can lead to physical exhilaration as well as an enhancement of the senses, for example, seeing more vibrant colors. It can also boost your morale, put you in a better mood, and just add a spring to your step.

- A medium dose of mushrooms is likely to produce some psychedelic effects, enhanced visual stimulation, and a greater feeling of euphoria.

- When consuming a high dose of mushrooms, you can expect a full-blown psychedelic experience with high perceptual and cognitive distortions! Get ready for kaleidoscope colors, the morphing of objects, and a sensory explosion as you start to peak. Take note that the effects often come in waves, so hold on and enjoy the ride!

- At heroic doses, there's not much you can do but allow the experience to wash over you. With such high amounts, shrooms are going to lead you, so get ready to follow them down the rabbit hole and into a whole other world!

- Never try to guess your dosage amount! Factors like your weight, an empty stomach, your mental state, the method of consumption, and if they are dried or ingested raw need to be considered.

- Use a mushroom calculator like the one I have inserted for you in the chapter to determine the exact amounts for your physical frame.

- Mushrooms can be consumed in many ways. Some people prefer eating them raw, while others infuse the dried, crushed fungi in teas, bake/cook with them (be aware of potential potency loss), or add them to their food. Try each method and see which one works best for your palate.

In conclusion, never forget to identify the specific species of shroom or truffle before ingesting it to make sure you know exactly how these psychedelics are going to affect you!

I hope this chapter has made you smarter and wiser. Next up, we will look at tripping tips and tricks!

Chapter 3: Tripped Up

My first mushroom trip was one of the most spiritual experiences I've had in my life.

After eating a dose of crushed, dried azzies (Psilocybe Azurescens), I started feeling like my body and mind seemed to be drifting apart. It is hard to describe my experience, but it was almost as if my consciousness had climbed out of my head and soared up into the sky, my soul becoming part of the earth.

Looking at my natural surroundings, I realized that the leaves in the trees became the most beautiful color I had ever seen. With the sun gleaming on them, they emitted a super green glow and I started to see the world through their perspective. It felt as though I was communicating directly with them as if they became flesh and my new reality. The plants had their own spirit, kind and caring.

Whatever it was in life that usually separated me from the outside world, "it" started to fall away. My sense of life and being part of the daily rat race faded. I had a much deeper connection with the world around me. I became filled with inner peace and self-love, freeing myself from the shackles of society. I knew immediately I would never view life in the same way. My fears and doubts seemed to disappear and for once I felt a sense of harmony!

Feeling the sand running through my fingers was an entirely new experience, almost like I felt it for the very first time. I became mesmerized as I watched the granules slipping down from the palm of my hand. There were moments I had the feeling I could see through my eyelids as if they were almost transparent! I remember closing my eyes and starting to visualize random memories, some of which I hadn't thought of for years, playing like a movie in front of me. Some fractal shapes and patterns appeared too, even while my eyes were closed.

As soon as I started to feel panicky over my lack of control, I discovered that all I had to do to re-establish a sense of "semi-normalcy" was to open my eyes. I started learning how to manage my experience. My legs felt like rubber and soon I began seeing very interesting visuals, sinking deeper into the imagery I was experiencing.

Tripping in nature was a great idea. I stared at two trees and had an epiphany. These old oaks had souls. I thought about all they had experienced and seen, what the world is doing to them, and eventually, how they will die.

I was no longer distant, my feelings pierced me more deeply, and I had a widespread sense of nostalgia throughout my trip. Eventually, the effects wore off and my experience started to fade. Very soon and without warning, my trip ended. I wish I could go back there, if only for a while longer, but I was already planning my next one.

There's a reason why people refer to tripping as a personal journey. Tripping is such an extensive experience that there is no real textbook explanation for exactly what will happen. This is why you have to prepare yourself to be ready for anything! Just surrender to your experience and understand that it will be profound for you and you alone.

No amount of planning can prepare you for the actual experience. It's one thing to tell yourself that you must be ready for anything before your trip, but it's something completely different once you are smack bang in the middle of it!

During your psychedelic journey, you might feel a peaceful sense of unity with something much bigger than yourself, or you could have a deep thoughtful conversation with an entity from another galaxy. There are so many components to unlock during a trip; just allow the shrooms to lead you.

That said, my friend Carla's trip was not as sunny and bright. In fact, she ended up sitting on the floor, staring at her watch crying as the seconds ticked by, realizing that with every hour passing, her life is getting shorter. Again, she thought about death, but this time it was her own mortality that negatively affected her. The clock's ticking became so loud it felt as if her ears were ringing. With every tick, more intense feelings of fear took hold of her. She felt that there was so much she still wanted to do, to experience, but she feared her life was passing by and she might leave this world, taking her last breath without accomplishing even half of what she set out to do. Let me add that once the effects wore off, she actually began laughing at herself, but her 'bad' trip sparked a new intensity inside her to accomplish her dreams and make a difference while she still could without any fear of death.

Knowing and acknowledging that anything could happen during your Psilocybin mushroom trip will make you feel more relaxed as soon as you start to feel the effects coming on. Stay positive and accept that your trip will probably lead you to the light but be aware that it might also lead you to darkness. Keep an open, peaceful mindset, and try your best to remember that if things do become uncomfortable your psychedelic experience is temporary, and the effects will eventually subside.

You might begin to see things in various colors or sounds, tastes and textures might become completely distorted. Your feelings and emotions may become exaggerated. You might feel like time has increased, slowed down, or stopped entirely.

These effects are but a guideline as what happens on a mushroom trip will vary from person to person as well as the dosage and the type of mushroom ingested.

Set and Setting

Imagine you are sitting in a small, dark room and as you begin to feel the effects of the shrooms you ingested you start to feel confined, out of breath, and anxious. You spiral down into a dark depression, and you have no idea how you are going to survive the next couple of hours. Just then, a close friend turns to you and reminds you that you are on a trip. Its purpose is to have fun and to open your mind to new experiences. You see them smile and almost in an instant, you begin to calm down and take control of your situation.

This short example above involves both set and setting. Two important aspects when planning your trip. Your mental state just before your psychedelic experience is known as your mindset. This can include but is not limited to your thoughts, feelings, desires, and mood beforehand. The setting is described as the physical and social environment you find yourself in during your psychedelic experience.

The people you surround yourself with and the place you choose to have your trip can have a massive impact on your psychedelic journey. You have to be positive, confident, and self-assured while preparing for your trip. You also need to feel completely comfortable with the environment you choose to trip in. Try to keep away from a negative state of consciousness and surround yourself with people who can comfort you if your experience becomes too intense to handle alone.

Tripping in nature is always a good idea as it offers lots of open, natural areas away from strangers and large groups of people. Sticking to people who you know, trust, and whose company you enjoy is also recommended, especially if you are tripping for the very first time. Tripping alone could be a frightening experience and it's always good to have someone around to support you who can get you out of a negative headspace if necessary.

If you prefer your own company, it's totally fine, but having a backup plan if events do turn sour is not a bad idea. Maybe just tell a close friend that you are planning a shroom trip so they can be aware. Call someone you trust before you take the shrooms or if the trip turns bad make sure you can get to a place where you feel safer.

Many of us expect our mushroom experience to be a positive one and most of the time they are, but there might be times when your psychedelic journey takes a downturn, and your trip is not as great as you expected. This is classified as a bad trip. It is fascinating, though, that many users have said that their bad trip actually turned out to be very interesting and educational.

That said, note that your psychedelic journey is called a trip because you experience the world so dramatically different that it can feel as if you have taken a trip to a brand new, mysteriously unusual world.

Signs You're Having a Bad Trip

It's very difficult to predict exactly how shrooms are going to affect you, which means that every user's trip symptoms will vary. Some might only experience a moderate effect, while other trips could turn intense and upsetting. You can be completely overwhelmed and frightened or you could be so fascinated with the intense hallucinations that your trip feels more like a movie that you are watching!

As already explained, every trip is a highly individualized experience, so I'll mention a few common aspects described by people who have had a bad trip.

Time Standing Still

Some users lose their perception of time completely and when you are stuck in a bad time warp of sorts, it can be super scary to think that you will be trapped like this forever! A tip to remember is to tell yourself this won't go on forever, even though it might not feel like it at the moment.

Paranoia

A bad trip could lead you to think that your friends can no longer be trusted. This can be very upsetting for both you and your companions. You might even feel that the whole world is bad and out to get you. Feelings of anxiety and paranoia could cause you to panic, wanting to run away from everyone around you. This is the last thing you should do though! A tip to remember is to try and tell yourself these people are your friends, they can be trusted, and have your best interest at heart. Again, you are under the influence of a mind-altering substance that will only last temporarily.

Hallucinations

Sometimes, users may hallucinate so hectically that they begin to believe that their delusions are real. Imagine you are seeing your friend's face melt off, watching them morph into a monster. If you realize that one of your friends is experiencing hallucinations, do your best to reassure them that what they are seeing is part of their trip.

Emotional Overload

Feelings of sadness and despair can reach new lows when tripping. Anxiety can turn into fear and fear can turn into sheer panic. It is difficult to remind yourself that you're not thinking clearly and to not indulge in these thoughts but try to remember that you're on an emotional runaway train.

Things will get better once the shrooms wear off! Your most intense period of tripping typically occurs an hour or two after the shrooms have been ingested. As time passes, the intensity will start to diminish, and the most extreme aspects of the trip will begin to cease.

Stopping a Bad Trip

Unfortunately, we have no "off switch" so once our bad trip starts the only thing we can do is to try and transform it into a more positive experience.

A few ideas to try to potentially help stop a bad trip include:

- Staying away from people and places that might upset you or freak you out.

- Don't take shrooms when you know something is bothering you.

- Avoid locations that may be over-stimulating, such as busy, brightly lit public areas.

- Stay close to people you trust.

- Ultimately, figure out what would make you feel safer or more comfortable. This can include listening to your favorite playlist, dancing, meditating, getting some fresh air, or even hiding under a blanket, like when you were a kid.

It's important to remember that you have the ability to turn your trip around. Many shroom users say their "bad trip" benefited them in some way, shape, or form. In Carla´s case, her bad trip made her hungry for life again. Now she wants to experience everything and feel fulfilled.

Ego Death

I have touched on this subject, but I feel Ego Death is a topic that needs more exploration, especially if you are going to use your shroom knowledge to trip.

So, what is Ego Death exactly? I will sum it up as a very intricate state where you disappear into oblivion, re-emerge from it, and do not exactly know where you went or what happened. Some psychonauts say it's like being reborn, but there truly are no words to accurately describe this state.

Imagine you just woke up from a dream you can't remember and suddenly you forgot your name, where you are, or what time it is. You know you are human, and you know you are on a planet that is one of many others spinning in space. Cue, "Ego Death."

You feel as if your mind has been wiped. You remember nothing. Neither your name, your sex nor your past. You have no hang-ups, no fears, and no extra emotional baggage. You might wonder where you are, what you are doing there, and where you are going. This type of total amnesia might frighten some or it might be a great relief to others.

A lack of answers to all your questions can become very alarming, especially if you believe that the state you are in will last forever. You might be on the opposite spectrum too, feeling elated and excited to begin a new life! Ego Death comes from the fact that many who experience it feel like they have died and were reborn into a new world, hence the name.

As with any mushroom trip, Ego Death is temporary, but as soon as you begin to remember you might become overwhelmed by sadness and pain as you "relive" many of the things that happened to you, both good and bad. This can obviously be a very painful event. First, you lose control, then yourself, and finally, you come back, feeling better on some level, even if you can't quite put your finger on why.

The trip gives you a different perspective. You become more self-aware, and you may handle situations differently. It's as if Ego Death helps you to cope with your reality, to confront your fears head-on. I mean, what bigger terror could there be than having to confront your biggest fear aka death? You conquered your anxieties and survived!

Absconding from reality and waking up in a world you now see from a whole new perspective can be scary. In order to rise and surpass the chains of reality, you must trust that this random series of neurochemical reactions is not only beneficial but also therapeutic. How you interpret your Ego Death experience and how you decide to incorporate it into your everyday thoughts and behaviors will ultimately be your downfall or your victory. The rebirth is the real journey.

Tolerance

Whether you're just inquisitive about tripping or you want to become a fully blown psychonaut, if you are interested in building a tolerance to shrooms here is what you need to know: If you take shrooms on Friday and you drop another dose right after, you're going to be very unsatisfied. Sadly, your brain won't allow your second trip, and here's why.

The word tolerance means how strongly your body responds to the effects of a drug. Over an extended period of time, your body becomes completely desensitized if you continuously use mushrooms. This means that taken repeatedly you will need more and more to experience the same effects.

If you were eager to drop a couple of doses of Psilocybin over the next few days, it's more than likely that you will not have the kind of success you were hoping for. Increasing the dose each time won't help either.

As soon as your brain is exposed to the first dose of Psilocin it won't accept any extra doses and you won't feel a thing. This is why it's recommended to wait at least 24 hours in between trips or even longer. If you can manage to take a breather for a couple of months in between doses, it allows your receptors to take in Psilocin again. A resting period also allows you to recuperate from any intense emotional, intellectual, or spiritual effects you might have previously experienced.

Psilocybin gets filtered out of the body in about 24 hours. Your body absorbs and breaks down Psilocybin quite quickly and it then gets secreted out of your system within a day. But this doesn't mean that you're ready for your next trip!

You must take a tolerance break. It makes no sense to keep on upping your dose to hardly feel anything. Our brains have a limit to how much we can consume before they create a neurological threshold requiring higher doses to create similar psychoactive effects.

It's vital to understand that tolerance does not equal addiction. Imagine the receptors in your brain as thousands of tiny open doors with your brain being a gigantic room. Throwing Psilocybin into one door instantly causes the other doors to close. So, after a while, it doesn't matter how much Psilocybin you ingest because all the doors in your brain are shut.

We recommend a 24-hour rest period in between microdoses, but on average, you should wait around 2 weeks for larger amounts to get the tolerance back to normal. Some users have said that they only waited a few days before tripping just as hard as they did initially. Your body is unique to you, so you'll have to see how long you need to wait between doses to avoid the tolerance building up.

Shroomy Summary

Let's sum up what we explored in this chapter:

- Experiences with magic mushrooms will vary based on the amount of Psilocybin you ultimately take, your personality, the mood you are in, and even your surroundings.

- Tripping can lead to changes in your sense of self and how you experience the world.

- Low doses of Psilocybin can lead to feelings of relaxation.

- During a trip, you can feel more open, more creative, and more grateful for the beauty around you.

- Higher doses may unlock elevated emotions, allowing users to become less narrow-minded with a more positive outlook on life.

- Some users seem to benefit from having their rigid mindset released during a trip, reducing hang-ups and bad habits.

- Positive beliefs before tripping will lead to more positive outcomes during your high.

- Magic mushrooms impact the part of the brain that controls abstract thinking and thought analysis, also known as the prefrontal cortex.

- Taking a high dose of shrooms can lead to an out-of-body experience.

- Shrooms induce encounters that can seem real but aren't.

- Some trips are very enjoyable, but others can lead to users feeling a bit anxious, especially if they start to lose control.

- During a challenging trip, try your best to figure out what the experience meant to you.

- Psilocybin can increase serotonin levels in the brain. If you are using medications that have a similar effect, taking Psilocybin along with these medications could lead to a spike in serotonin levels, causing serious side effects.

- Users who might have a mental health condition face a higher risk of having a bad trip.

- Some people who use too much Psilocybin may need to go to the emergency room to eradicate adverse effects.

- Do not consume mushrooms if you are going through a personal crisis in your life; the chances of having a "bad trip" are much higher if you do.

- Bad or challenging trips can and do happen. If you agree to be a sitter for a friend and you notice them starting to panic, becoming anxious, or in danger of harming themselves or others, find medical help right away.

- Everyone will experience a wide variety of emotions while on shrooms, so your trip will feel completely different from somebody else's, even if you both consumed the same species and dose.

I have taught you about shrooms, their effects, benefits, risks, and tripping. It's time to move on and teach you the skills needed to grow your own!

Chapter 4: Grow Like a Pro!

"Fungi constitute the most poorly understood and underappreciated kingdom of life on Earth."-Michael Pollan

People grow magic mushrooms for lots of reasons and so can you! One of the major benefits of growing your own includes much less uncertainty than if you go foraging for them and not being sure what you might be ingesting.

Cultivating your own strain of shrooms leaves you in complete control during the production process. It might feel a bit overwhelming when starting with mushroom cultivation, but fortunately growing your own shroom babies is quite easy and very straightforward!

Magic mushrooms can be cultivated outdoors in ready-made mushroom beds or grown inside by the method known as hydroponics.

The main thing to remember is that your mushroom is a magic truffle's (mycelium) fruiting body. The point of the mycelium is to grow its fruit, aka the mushroom, which produces spores and then reproduces by releasing the seeds into new areas.

Your goal then would be to help your mycelium expand as far and as wide as possible. This means that you will have to give it a substantial food supply and make sure it stays healthy and happy! Before you think, "Wow, this is simple enough," be warned that bacteria can contaminate your mycelium in the blink of an eye, which will leave your shrooms sick and unsafe to ingest.

It would be ideal if you can set up a small grower's station to reduce the risk of contamination. Some essentials would include HEPA filters and fans, big plastic carts that can act as temporary sterile areas, and a bucket-load of isopropyl alcohol. Most of these tools can be sourced online or even at your local hardware store.

For those more dedicated, you can build your own mushroom lab! I will explain how in a minute, but for now, I just want you to focus on getting your mycelium to a point where it has grown enough to have a healthy, strong immune system so it can fight off any unwelcome microbes.

The Cultivation Process

Farming will begin with a culture sample, live specimen, or a pre-manufactured spore print. These three options are your starting point. They are similar to planting seeds in the garden, yet much, much smaller and more delicate. Once you have your spores you will have to make them comfy, nestling them into their new home. They will need food to grow just like any infant. Your most common food source for feeding your mycelium baby is nutrient-rich agar, pre-prepared in a glass jar. You can start by putting your "seeds" in a petri-dish first so they can grow a little bit bigger before transferring them into their glass jar homes.

After "planting" your spores, the mycelium will start to grow, and you will begin to notice a web of white, fuzzy fibers that almost look like root hairs filling up their crib. If your babies survive you can now call yourself a proud parent and name your little ones! If no bacteria infect them and they continue to grow, you can transplant them into bigger wide-mouthed glass jars prepared with grains. Always remember to keep everything as sterile as possible! This is where temperature control comes in. If done correctly, your mycelium will grow like wildfire. This process is known as spawning.

You can now choose to follow one of a few routes.

The Fungi Life Cycle

Before growing your own mushrooms at home, you need to know the basics of the fungi life cycle.

Many of us think of a mushroom as the stem and the cap, but there is actually an entire network growing underneath known as mycelium. The mycelium is the plant and the shrooms you see growing are the fruits it produces.

Like any mushroom, the caps and stems are the only phases of the life cycle we see. So how do mushrooms begin to grow? In other life forms, the male sperm enters the female's egg creating an embryo. In the fungi life cycle, two nuclei lay side by side in one cell for a period of time. Eventually, the cell fuses and fertilization occurs. An interesting fact is that the fertilization stage remains present in most of the fungi's fruiting bodies. Its underside comprises a gilled tissue. If you look at the bottom of a mushroom cap, you'll notice these gills.

The function of the gills is to increase the surface area of the mushroom's underside, which in turn generates many spores, improving the fungi's chances of reproducing as much as possible. The spores are then released from under the gills and carried by the wind to a new growing spot. Every spore contains a nucleus, but not every one of them becomes a new organism. Therefore, the mushroom lets go of millions of spores. One in a thousand might germinate, which then develops into the fine tube-like hairs we mentioned growing in the petri-dish. Eventually, the fibers turn into a web-like structure called mycelium. When two mycelia of opposite mating types come into contact, their cells fuse, new nuclei lie next to each other, and the life cycle begins all over again!

The mycelium starts to grow and will eventually develop fruiting bodies above the ground known as shrooms.

The Fungi Life Cycle in Simpler Terms:

1. The mature mushroom drops its spores.

2. The spores get carried by the wind and fall to the ground.

3. The spores germinate in the soil.

4. The newly germinated spores meet compatible spores from the opposite sex.

5. Mycelium is born.

6. Pinheads are created.

7. They grow into tiny mushrooms.

8. The fruiting bodies start to grow and mature.

9. The fully grown mushroom is formed.

10. Once mature, the mushroom releases its spores.

11. The cycle begins again.

Growing Mushrooms

Now that you know a bit more about the fungi life cycle, I think you might be ready to grow your own! If you are wondering how long this process is going to take before you have a nice sturdy shroom crop, let me give you a rundown of the approximate timeline.

For your shrooms to germinate, you will have to wait about a week. After two weeks to a month, your birthing cake of mycelium will have colonized completely. The fruiting cycle takes another two weeks and after six to eight weeks you should have fully grown shrooms.

Mushrooms need specific conditions to grow, conditions that involve the soil or substrate, its nutrient concentration, pH, temperature, humidity, light, ventilation, etc. And this varies for each strain. If these conditions are met and there is no threat of mold spores and other contaminants, they will develop successfully. The main reason beginner growers fail is due to contamination, so pay special attention to this.

Different Growing Methods

I am going to provide you with a few different ways to grow your magic mushrooms, so you can decide which approach will work best for you. I would have loved to put plenty of images to be more practical, these images can be found easily on the internet, but unfortunately, it has been complicated due to the copyright of the images, lack of image contributors, and because I haven't been able to cultivate shrooms myself while writing this book due to my nomadic lifestyle. Despite this, I have decided to go ahead with it, putting all my effort into describing the steps as best I can, with accurate and truthful information. If this book is successful, I may end up with a lot of contributor images in my email, who knows?

Any proven method followed properly will work and it is critical to keep the required tools and areas clean. I decided to include several methods, from beginner to advanced.

Let me add a note of caution here: When buying spores online, make sure you are dealing with a reputable supplier. The internet makes it easy for people to get scammed and many mushroom cultivators have reported getting spore syringes that only contained water as well as contaminated samples or misdiagnosed specimens. Take a look at Chapter Eight where I explain exactly what to look for when choosing the right supplier on the web. Okay, let's get back to growing with our first method.

PF Tek Method

The acronym PF Tek stands for "Psilocybe Fanaticus Technique." It is said to be one of the best cultivation methods for beginner growers to get used to the idea of strict sterilization and small-scale spawn production.

The tools needed are readily available and your shroom substrate primarily consists of brown rice flour and vermiculite.

As soon as your substrate has been fully colonized, the brown rice flour cakes can either be fruited directly, or you can mix your spawn with a bulk substrate to produce much larger flushes.

Equipment Needed:

- lighter

- gloves (latex)

- paper towels

- one can of disinfectant spray

- rubbing alcohol

- hypodermic needles that fit your syringe

- spray bottle

- plastic tub with a lid (I either use a 32-quart medium tub dimensions: 18.85 in. L x 14.38 in. W x 10.5 in. H or a 54-quart large tub dimensions: 22.5 in. x 16 in. x 13 in.)

- temperature gauge

- vermiculite

- perlite

- hydrogen peroxide 3%

- mason jar

- aluminum foil

- round metal grid or jar lid rings

- mask

- hammer and nails

- pressure cooker or large pot.

The First Stage:

The process starts with a syringe filled with spores, which I will teach you how to make in Chapter 5. And as a standard measure, you will require a mason jar filled with grains like brown rice flour for each cubic centimeter in your syringe. This means if your syringe holds 10 cubic centimeters (10 milliliters) you need to prepare ten mason jars (250 ml standard size).

Your jars have to be sterile to ensure no bacteria infect your spores, so follow an intense sterilization process beforehand.

Cultivation Stage

You are now ready to cultivate your birthing cake. It is called a cake because once your mycelium has fully colonized the mason jar and you remove it, the mycelium should hold together without breaking easily.

Disinfect Properly

Fungi grow in moist, dark places and so do many bacteria. Throughout your cultivating journey, your number one enemy is contamination. Bacteria can spread so quickly that one microorganism could multiply and kill your mushrooms, even before they've had a chance to sprout!

Decide on one particular room to set up your laboratory and get ready to prep that space. Put on your mask, gather all the tools I mentioned earlier, and enter your chosen area. Close the door and begin by spraying everything using your disinfectant. Put on your gloves, grab your jars, and wipe each one carefully using rubbing alcohol and a paper towel.

Ingredients For Your Jars

The proportion of ingredients for each jar includes two parts vermiculite, one part of brown rice flour, and one-part water. And as an optional additive, some growers use one teaspoonful of gypsum if you're making five jars; gypsum contains calcium and other minerals.

- ¼ cup vermiculite for one jar + extra

- ¼ cup drinking water for one jar

- ¼ cup organic brown rice flour for one jar

Begin with the two parts vermiculite. Now add one part water and mix thoroughly. The vermiculite must be wet, but make sure there is no excess water at the bottom of your bowl. If your mix is too dry, add more water until you reach the right consistency.

Finally, add one part of brown rice flour and mix thoroughly. Do not compress the mixture. It must have an airy, fluffy consistency. Allow the flour to coat your vermiculite.

Fill each jar with your mixture, leaving a clear and clean space of about three cm (one inch) at the top of the jar. This part will be filled with dry vermiculite. The dry vermiculite works as a safety barrier. Cover each one of your lids with a piece of tin foil.

Sterilize

If your jars have metal lids, make two to four holes beforehand with a hammer and a nail (1/8 drill bit, 0.8 mm), spacing them equally around the edge (picture below). Tear off a nice size square of tin foil and fold it in half. Make sure it's large enough to cover your jar's mouth and runs down each side about half the height of the jar. Place the foil over your jar lid and scrunch it together so it fits tightly all around. Tear off a second piece of tin foil and cover your whole jar. Repeat these steps with all your jars.

Pressure Cooker

If you are fortunate enough to own a pressure cooker, fill the bottom part with 2.5 cm of water. Be careful not to pour in too much water because when the cooker starts to boil and the levels are too high, it might throw your jars off balance causing them to break. Stack all your jars inside the pressure cooker. Make sure your jars are elevated from the bottom of the pressure cooker with a round metal grid or with jar lid rings underneath each one to avoid them from cracking or burning. Do this gently so as not to tear the tin foil that they are wrapped in. Place the lid on and bring the cooker to a slow boil over the next 15 minutes until it reaches 15 psi. If you boil the water too quickly, you run the risk of cracking your glass jars! So be gentle and careful during the heating stage. As soon as the pressure cooker releases its steam, reduce the heat until the steam escapes every so often. Leave it to simmer for 45 minutes and leave it to cool to room temperature overnight.

Using a Pot

You will need a round metal rack to place at the bottom of your large pot. Pour water into the pot until the bottom is filled up to 2.5 cm. Stack your jars gently onto the metal rack, making sure not to damage the tin foil seal around them.

Place the lid on and slowly bring your pot to a boil using medium heat. Once it starts boiling, reduce the temperature, so your pot boils slowly. Leave it boiling for 90 minutes but check your water levels occasionally, as it will evaporate because your pot does not have a tight-fitting seal as a pressure cooker does.

Top up your levels with pre-boiled water from your kettle but make sure the water is not too hot causing your jars to crack. After 90 minutes you can switch off your heat and leave your bottles in the pot to cool for a minimum of five hours. I recommend leaving your jars to cool overnight.

Inoculation

Mist the jars with 70% alcohol, remove the foil, and inject your spores into your jars below the dry vermiculite layer.

If you bought new, sealed hypodermic needles they should be sterile, but just to make sure, you can use your lighter to heat your needles until the tip starts to glow red. Keep your needle in your hands, if you put it down you will have to sterilize it again. Wait for your needle to cool. Get your syringe filled with your mushroom spores and give it one or two good shakes so they can spread evenly. Insert your needle, suck up one cubic centimeter (one milliliter) of spores and inject it into one of your mason jars. Continue filling your jars until all the liquid has been used. Remember to sterilize your needle every time before you fill a new jar.

Incubation

Pack all your mason jars carefully in a cardboard box, seal the box, and place the box in a dark, warm area. The best temperature for a birthing cake to grow is between 80 and 85°F, 70 °F can be fine, but it will grow slower. Leave the box for five days and NO PEEKING! You can open your cardboard box on day six and if you see a fuzzy white substance in your jars, you have become the proud parent of ten newly born mycelium cakes! If you notice any green, pink or black blotches in your jar your mycelium has been infected and you should get rid of it immediately. If you find no signs of contamination, leave the jars for another two to four weeks minimum. It is suggested to leave them until the mycelium has colonized the entire jar until it is full.

Moving Your Birthing Cake

As soon as there is no more space for your mycelium to grow in its jar house, it has to be transferred to its fruiting chamber where it will start to sprout mushrooms. Before moving them, they will have to be "bathed" in sterilized water, sterilization is always critical. Your birthing cakes have been kept in an airtight container for weeks, which means they have already used up all the moisture and they are thirsty as hell!

Put on new latex gloves after washing your hands thoroughly and loosen your first jar's lid. You will have to shake your jar to loosen the birthing cake and get it out. Try your best to touch your cake as little as possible. Place the cake into the baggie or your container and continue with the rest of your jars until all your cakes have been packed into your tub or a baggie. Fill the tub or baggies as full as you can get them with filtered water and seal it. Place your cakes in your fridge and leave them to soak for 12 to 24 hours.

Final Move

Sterilize the container and drill 6mm holes (1/4" drill bit) in all six sides, spaced out two inches. Get a spray bottle and fill it with one part hydrogen peroxide and ten parts water. Spread a nice thick layer of perlite (one to two inches) on the bottom of the container or growing chamber. You need to keep your bottom layer moist to maintain the humidity so spray it regularly with the solution you made in your bottle. A good tip to remember is to look for water droplets forming inside your container. This means condensation is taking place and you are on the right track. Perfect conditions include high humidity (>80%) and a temperature of between 20–28 °C (68–82°F).

Use the lids from your mason jars as a bed for each cake, placing them into the perlite, make sure they are at least one inch apart from one another to ensure enough growing room for your mushrooms to sprout from each cake. If you look closely, you might see tiny mushroom sprouts known as pins forming on each cake, if this is the case you did well, and your cakes will produce fruiting bodies soon! Some species pin much later than others, but if you notice one jar has fewer pins than the rest, wrap it in a plastic bag and put it in the fridge or cold exposure overnight to "activate" the process.

Another method to ensure healthy cakes is to smell them. If they have a foul odor, they have most likely been infected with bacteria and should not be used to sprout mushrooms. The only thing left to do now is to place the lid on your growing chamber and leave it in an area with enough indirect sunlight or white fluorescent light for 4-12 hours a day, and good ventilation.

Spritz your bottom layer (only the layer) three or four times daily. Make sure it stays moist. It should not be lower than 85%. If your humidity levels are lower than that, spray your layer more often.

As soon as your mycelium cakes are full of mushrooms, you can harvest them by snapping each one off at the base of the stem. Congratulations, you have managed to harvest your first flush! Do you know what the best part is? You can use your birthing cakes again to produce a new harvest of shrooms!

Ten mason jars produce ten birthing cakes; if you are uncertain about your growing skills, you can start with fewer jars. After harvesting your mushrooms, they should stay fresh for up to two weeks if you keep them in your fridge. It is best to dry your excess produce as dried mushrooms can hold for years. If you freeze them once they're fully dried, they will hold almost indefinitely!

Uncle Ben Tek (Spider-Man Tek) Method

The PF Tek method is by far the most popular way to grow shrooms, especially if you are a first-time grower. Many people have also had great success with the Uncle Ben Tek method, so I figured I'll give you growing instructions for this method as well.

Shopping List:

- Pre-cooked brown rice in a bag. Uncle Ben's Rice is one example of a brand, but you can find similar brands. Note instant rice or minute rice will not work! You are looking for rice that you can eat almost straight out of the bag, fully cooked and sterilized so it's safe to eat. You do not have to heat the rice, keep it at room temperature.

- Your preferred spore solution

- A pair of scissors

- Rubbing alcohol

- Micropore tape

- Still air box

Instructions:

Use your fingers to break up the rice while still in the bag. Sterilize the outside of your bag with rubbing alcohol or any other strong disinfectant solution. Sterilize your scissors and cut off one corner of the bag. Sterilize your syringe needle by heating it with your lighter as mentioned in the PF Tek method.

Take your spore solution and inject one cubic centimeter of it into your rice bag. Tape the bag closed with micropore tape. You can also punch two holes on either side of the bag and cover them with tape. The point is to give your mycelium some air to breathe.

You need to store your bags in an area with a stable temperature like your wardrobe or a closet. Mycelium colonizes quickly with stable temperatures of 24°C (75°F). Wait for your mycelium to grow. Give it a good shake after a third of the bag has been colonized and wait for a minimum of seven days after inoculation. If there are large clumps of rice, break them up using your fingers.

As soon as the entire bag has been colonized and there is no green, yellow or red colors, which means contamination, you can move on to the fruiting stage!

Fruiting Phase

Fruiting, also known as spawning to bulk, means that you are going to take your colonized bags of rice, mix them with a substrate, and move them into a plastic tub so you can grow mushrooms.

What you will need:

- Bucket with lid

- Clear plastic tub - Your monotub size will depend on your substrate and your mushroom spawn. Your mixed substrate should cover three to five inches of the tub from the bottom.

- Coco coir

- Spray Bottle

- LED lights

Mixing Ratios

One six-quart tub (Dimensions: 13 5/8 in. x 8 ¼ in. x 4 7/8 in. will hold two bags of colonized rice. A great trick for mixing a near-perfect "field capacity" is to use a 1:1

ratio, meaning 50 grams of compact, dry coco coir per bag of rice. (The coir increases in weight once you add water, so 50 grams will become 250 grams, which is the exact amount of rice in your Uncle Ben's rice bag). This means you will need 100 grams of coco coir for two bags of rice. Do not worry about adding too much water, you will squeeze out any excess water before you add it to your tub. Use the 1:1 ratio to calculate how much coco coir you'll need to spawn your number of bags.

Instructions

Wipe down your bucket with rubbing alcohol and leave it to dry. Place your coco coir in your bucket. Boil a gallon of water and pour little by little onto the coco coir, breaking it up. Continue adding water until your coir is mushy, but not too watery. Once it cools down, put on your gloves to ensure sterile conditions and squeeze out the water. Mix thoroughly and close with the lid.

As mentioned before with the PF Tek method, make sure your prep areas are as clean as possible. Wipe everything down with rubbing alcohol.

After your tub has been sterilized, you can begin the spawning process. Cut open your rice bags and break them up into fine grains, mixing thoroughly with half of your coco coir substrate, making the first layer without compressing it too much. Then add the rest of the coir to cover the top surface. Put on your tub's lid and place it in a dark, humid area. After three to seven days, if you notice pins beginning to form you can move on to the fruiting stage.

Fruiting

Once you get to this stage you can relax a bit. Threats of contamination are far less, and you have overcome the biggest bump in the cultivation process. Your little mushroom pins now need air and moisture. Open your tub's lid and turn it upside down so there is a tiny air gap between the lid and your tub. Now that they can breathe, your next step would be to ensure they consume enough water. If you notice tiny droplets of water on the surface of your tub, the conditions are good. If not, you'll have to mist your babies with the spray bottle. Do not mist too much or else they will drown; your tub must be moist but not filled with water pools anywhere. If you do happen to spray too much water, use a cloth to soak up most of the moisture. Keep your spray bottle at a good distance when misting. The drops must fall gently, so don't spray up close. When you can see your mushroom pins clearly, you can buy some inexpensive LED lights and fasten them to the ceiling of your growing room. Try to install the LED lights directly above your monotub. This can be done in any number of ways depending on your setup. You want to emulate daylight, so the lights only need to burn for 12 to 18 hours at a time. Continue misting your shrooms if they look dry, but make sure they are not too wet! Watch your babies grow until they are fully formed mushrooms ready for picking!

Monotub Tek

This method is for serious growers who want an abundant harvest at a low cost. All you need is a tub or a container that you can modify to create the perfect mini-climate for your mushrooms. The monotub ensures high humidity levels, while the holes drilled in the container allow for appropriate air ventilation and gas exchange.

The idea of monotub cultivation is for your mycelium to colonize every part of your substrate, growing into a massive network and producing a large number of shrooms. Many growers prefer this method because they only need to focus on one container that provides a bountiful yield. It's quite affordable and easy to do. So, let's get going!

Equipment Needed:

To build your monotub you will need the following:

- 55- to 60-liter tub container

- large tote

- bucket

- big spoon or stick

- large pressure cooker or large pot

- micropore tape

- aluminum foil

- large oven bag

- lighter

- bin bag

- poly-fil

- isopropyl alcohol

- spray bottle

To prepare your substrate, you will need the following.

- 1 liter of water

- 2.5 liters of mushroom spawn

- 2.5 liters of unrefined vermiculite

- 2 liters of cow manure

- one-quarter of a brick of coco coir

- hydrated lime

This is your basic recipe. You can go as big as you want by bulking up your ingredients, just stick to the ratios and proportions!

Building Time!

Once you have gathered all your supplies, it's time to build your monotub and grow your shrooms!

To construct your monotub start by measuring 12 centimeters/4.7 inches from the bottom of your container and mark it. Our substrate level has to be below this mark and the air holes above. Your hole sizes need to be as close to 38 millimeters as possible. Ten holes around the four side faces are enough.

Now add a tub liner. This is where you use the black bin bag. The point of the liner is to reduce side pinning. Lay your trash bag inside the tub. It's going to be a bit big, so cut off the top beforehand to make sure it fits snugly right underneath your air holes. Take some rubbing alcohol or any other type of disinfectant and properly sterilize your tub and any tools you still need. This means washing your hands too! The cleaner your area and your equipment are, the lower the chance of your crop becoming contaminated. Congratulations, your monotub is complete!

Substrate

Let's move on to adding the substrate. You know by now that your shrooms need a substrate to feed on.

Throw half a brick of coco coir in your bucket and pour one liter of boiled water into the bucket as well. Cover your bucket and leave it to sit for at least 15 minutes. Use your spoon or stick to stir your mixture until it has broken up evenly. Allow your mixture to sit for another hour.

Take your cow manure, one teaspoon of the hydrated lime, and 2.5 liters of coarse vermiculite and add them together in your large tote. Mix carefully. Add the coco coir blend and mix again. You have now prepared your substrate!

Take an oven bag and fill it with your substrate. Press out any excess air and seal it. Make a couple of holes in the bag and cover each one with your micropore tape. Place your bag into your large pressure cooker and allow it to boil at 103Pa for a minimum of 90 minutes. Leave your bag in the cooker overnight to cool down.

Spawning

One way to mix our substrate and spawn without involving the hands is distributing a quarter of our mushroom spawn as evenly as possible, then grabbing your bag out of the cooker, and adding another quarter into your monotub. Keep alternating quarters until finished. Seal the holes on the side faces of the tub with Poly-Fil, or micropore tape. Press the lid on and allow your spawn to colonize for at least 10-14 days.

Fruiting

Once your spawn has colonized, add your casing layer by mixing three parts of vermiculite with one part of water until the vermiculite becomes hydrated. Spread the casing over your tub to form a 0.5 inch/1.5 cm layer on top. Gently mist the sides of your tub with your spray bottle and close the lid.

For the fruiting phase, it's best to find an area with enough ambient light, but no direct sunlight to place your monotub in. Try to keep a constant temperature of 21°C (69.8°F) and if you have a fan use it to produce a nice continuous flow of fresh air to bring down the humidity and temperature to "activate" the fruiting process. Your pins should begin to grow and mature within two weeks!

Harvesting

You know it's time to harvest when your shrooms are almost fully grown, but just before the veils underneath the caps start to break open.

Growing Mushrooms Using Agar

The method we will be exploring includes steps to grow your very own outdoor mushroom patch using agar.

You might have learned about agar in your biology class at school. If your teacher allowed you to look through a microscope at microorganisms in a petri dish, agar was probably used to grow them. Agar is a jelly-like product made from red seaweed that is used as a thickener or an alternative to gelatin when baking.

It is the perfect environment in which to grow magic mushroom cultures. It's not difficult to obtain as it's mostly sold in powder form at your local health shop. Agar alone won't be enough to grow your cultures because on its own it provides no nourishment to your spawn. Various nutrients have to be added with the most popular being malt sugar and yeast extract.

Malt Extract Agar recipe

- 1 gram/¼ tsp of malt extract syrup
- 5 grams/1 tsp of agar powder
- 200 ml of water

Additional Tools

- pressure cooker
- 350 ml glass jars
- thermometer
- cling wrap cut to 45 mm in length
- tiny plastic containers to use as Petri dishes
- spore print or spore syringe
- scalpel, or sharp knife

- 70% alcohol or methylated spirits

- hydrogen peroxide at a three percent concentration

- pressure cooker

- thin glass rod

- still air box

Before we go any further, let's build our Still Air Box first. You can either use a 53-quart plastic storage tub or larger and add a one-kilogram tomato tin to cut the breathing holes with. Storage tubs can be brittle so heat your tomato tin and use it to cut or melt two holes into the sides of your storage tub.

Making Agar Plates

Measure out 200 ml of liquid and pour it into your glass jar. Grab a saucepan and use it to create a water bath for your jar. Add water to the saucepan and bring it to a boil, your jar might explode if too hot, so place it into the saucepan before the water heats up to ensure an even spread of heat. Use your thermometer and wait until the liquid in your jar reaches 80°C (176°F). Add the malt and then the agar powder. Mix properly to ensure everything is well dissolved. Add the agar powder slowly while stirring the entire time. Agar tends to stick, and if not stirred thoroughly it will start forming gelatinous chunks. After the agar is dissolved, you can cover your jar with some aluminum foil and put it into the pressure cooker at 15 psi to cook for 20 minutes. This is to sterilize your mixture.

Your next move must happen quickly. As soon as your pressure cooker has been boiling for 20 minutes, depressurize it and move the agar to the Still Air Box as fast as possible. Agar sets quickly, so sterilize your Still Air Box and the remainder of your tools while the mixture is in the pressure cooker. If you are using tiny takeaway sauce containers, sterilize them beforehand and set them up so you can pour your agar mixture into each one with ease. Pour your agar into your plates (sauce containers) when it has cooled a bit, but it's not set yet. You might need some practice with this step, but after a few attempts, you should be a pro!

Germinating Spores

Inject a drop or two of your spores from your syringe onto your agar and spread it all across the surface of your plate. You can also scrape some spores off your spore print and spread them across your plate. Seal your plates with the cling wrap that you sterilized with paraffin or alcohol beforehand and place them in sealable plastic baggies for additional protection. Keep your agar plates in a container at room temperature or between 18 to 26°C (64.4 to 78.8°F). Label your plates with the spore's name, date, and agar solution used. Now you wait.

Your spores will start to germinate in about a week and after two weeks you should see them growing quite clearly. Your mycelium will look like tiny white tufts streaking all along your plates. If you notice any white spots, gray or yellow spots your culture is contaminated.

If you end up with healthy mycelium that covers the entire surface of your agar well done! You are now ready to transfer your mycelium to new agar plates by cutting tiny triangles or squares from along the edge of your plate to your new agar plates to get better rhizomorphic growth, or to a spawn bag. You can store your Petri dishes/plates in the fridge as long as they are covered and remain below the freezing point.

Cloning with Agar

If you look closely at a mushroom, you will see it is made up of fibers called hyphae. You can take a small piece of this hyphae as a sample and put it on agar, and it will start growing! This is called tissue culture, which means using samples from fresh mushrooms to create mycelium and produce new cultures. Tissue cultures have much less contamination risk and are great for when you want to reproduce a strong, potent strain.

For you to dissect your magic mushroom, you will first have to sterilize your knife or scalpel with your burner or lighter and allow the blade to cool down. Choose the mushroom you are going to sacrifice and wipe it down with a paper towel previously soaked in alcohol. The next step is taking the sample from the inside of the fruit. To reduce the risk of contamination, simply tear off a part of the cap (or slice the mushroom in half if too small) and take the sample from the inner part. Make sure you keep all the tools sterilized.

Now gently place the sample onto the peroxide agar and seal with cling wrap. In approximately seven to 14 days, you'll notice the clone turning hairy and then starting to expand across the entire surface of your petri dish. You can clone as many tissue samples as you want using this technique!

You can use any agar recipe with a three percent hydrogen peroxide solution to create your tissue cultures or clones. Follow the same instructions we gave for creating a spore culture but add two milliliters of H_2O_2 to the agar once it has cooled to 45 to 55°C (113 to 131°F).

A side note: It is not necessary to use the peroxide Agar Tek to clone samples; you can grow them on standard agar too, as long as you enforce strict sterile conditions as you go.

Grow Kit

The last method you can choose includes using a grow kit. These kits offer beginners a quick and easy way to grow shrooms at home. One of the main reasons pro-growers don't like using these kits is that they don't know what type of strain they will be getting or exactly which species they are working with.

Grow kits include most of the basic tools required, such as a fully colonized substrate, a growth container, and instructions to get started. Additional tools to have include gloves and a misting/spray bottle. Some growers also opt for a heat mat and a heat guard as well as a hygrometer, but these three are optional.

Mushroom kits are a great way to hone your skills if you are a first-time grower because it cuts out the most difficult part of cultivation. Your kit comes complete with a fully colonized substrate, which means that you can skip the inoculation period completely. You can move straight to the fruiting phase and contamination is far less likely.

Each kit differs, but all of them work on the same principle. You need to expose your mycelium to water and air to trigger the fruiting phase. For the next couple of weeks, your job will be to keep your mycelium in a humid environment, allowing it some fresh air once a day. Your kit will come with instructions on how to do this safely. Manuals can also be downloaded online for more directions once you know the brand of kit you will be using.

A kit is, of course, more expensive than using the PF Tek method I explained earlier, but your chances of harvesting healthy, fully-grown mushrooms are much higher and you are almost guaranteed many memorable trips to come!

There are no other real downsides to this option. If you would like to be part of the entire process from inoculation to harvesting, then a growth kit will not be for you.

Growing Mushrooms Outdoors

It doesn't really matter which bulk spawn method you choose as long as the end result is the same. As soon as you have a bag or jar of fully colonized grains, it can be added to a larger amount of sawdust or beech wood chips to further spread the mycelium. Take note that you are planning to grow fungi outdoors, which means that there is a very high risk of contamination involved. You need to take great care to ensure your mushroom crop stays healthy.

You will need:

- your bulk grain spawn

- a plastic bag

- a 10-liter bag of beech wood chips or two 5-liter bags

- a cardboard box – medium (30 cm high and 30 cm wide)

- a large bucket

- a one-liter plastic container with a lid

- a utensil fork

- boiling water

Instructions

Fill your one-liter plastic container ¾ full with your beechwood chips. Add boiling water and leave to cool for a minimum of 12 hours. Once cooled, drain the excess water left behind. Put on gloves and gently break up your mycelium cake in your plastic bag. Use the "break and shake" method, mixing all the ingredients gently. Now distribute the contents of the bag evenly into your container, emptying it completely. Use a sterile fork and mix the mycelium with the wood chips in the container. Cover the mixture with a piece of wet cardboard, and cut it to fit over your container, but don't cut it too small because you are going to put the lid over the cardboard. It needs to fit loosely because your mixture needs air, so this time it must not be airtight! The lid is only used as a barrier to keep foreign objects out.

Leave the container in a clean dark storage area free from dust and direct sunlight for 30 days. After a month, you should notice that the wood chips, as well as the pieces of mycelium, have turned white. This means that full inoculation took place, and you can now move your mixture outside.

Add the leftover beechwood chips from your 10-liter bag into a large bucket filling it ¾ full and then add boiling water again. Allow to cool for 12 hours and drain just as you did before. Place the drained beechwood chips and

113

your inoculated blend in your container into a new cardboard box and mix them together using a sterile fork. Spread out your mix evenly. Your box is now ready to be buried outside in an area you have chosen beforehand. Remember your mushrooms don't like direct sunlight, so choose a space with enough heat but no harsh sun rays. Add a 1 cm/0.3-inch layer of moist soil over the top of your mixture and water your patch if you feel the soil has become too dry.

The last step is to cover your growing area with a fresh layer of wood chips as soon as the season starts to change and summer turns to autumn. If you look after your patch, giving it enough water and love, you should be blessed with a beautiful harvest (flush) of shrooms. Simply pull them out of the ground by hand and enjoy them!

Shroomy Summary

Here are a few tips to remember while growing your magic mushrooms:

- Only buy your mushroom spores from reputable suppliers.

- Fungi do not extract any nutrients from the sun. They do not have to be grown in total darkness, but you have to keep them out of direct sunlight.

- The benefit of growing mushrooms in the dark is that they can preserve moisture that the spores need to reproduce.

- Mushrooms receive the nutrients they require from organic materials. They extract the nutrients they need from the beechwood chips or substrate mixtures that they're growing in.

- Bacteria and mold love to multiply in conditions where you cultivate your shrooms, so it's critical to ensure good hygiene and keep your environment as sterile as possible.

- If you want your mushrooms to grow at a steady pace, your environment must provide enough moisture and heat so that their life cycle can run its course.

- Don't wait for your shrooms to reach the end of their growth cycle, they'll start to lose potency once they mature beyond a certain point.

- Mycelium cakes are typically white (depending on the species), but if you notice a green mold, they have likely been contaminated; discard them immediately.

- Every birthing cake can have multiple harvests; leave your mycelium cake in water for 24 hours and return it to its fruiting chamber to begin a new crop. Each cake can fruit 2-3 times.

If you haven't started growing, get going! In the next chapter, you will learn how to make your own spore syringe. In Chapter six, we will cover the harvest, drying methods, and all things related to fungal spores. So, think of a name for your babies, who knows you might be able to create your own new strain! Excited yet?

Chapter 5: Culture Shock

"Before Wasson, nobody took the mushrooms only to find God. They were always taken for the sick to get well."–Maria Sabina

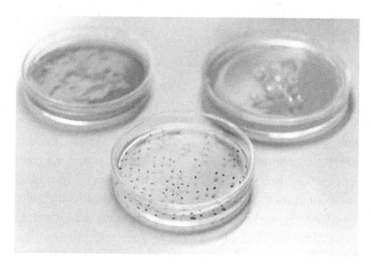

Spore Print

A mushroom spore is just like a seed. You plant seeds to grow plants, so you will need spores to grow your shrooms.

What you see in the image below is what is called a spore print. This is a sample of the Psilocybe species, the color should be blackish or very dark purple-brown.

If you have managed to grow your first shroom yield using a spore syringe it is a good idea to store some of the spores from your cultivated crop. When shrooms start to produce and distribute their spores you will notice the shrooms next to them are covered in a black oily substance. This might leave you wondering what went wrong and if they are contaminated. No, it's not a type of bacteria, it's their seeds. Once your shroom has begun dropping its spores, the fewer spores will be on your print, the higher your chances of contamination will be, and your crop might fail because of impure prints. Therefore, we recommend that you harvest your shrooms before they get to this stage.

Creating your own spore print is relatively easy and straightforward. Once you have your print, you can either mix the spores with distilled water and your substrate or you can make your own spore syringe. I am going to first explain the print and then we can move on to the liquid syringe technique. You can make your print on various mediums but for this task, we will be using aluminum foil. Foil is the most preferred medium because it is light, cheap, and clean. Remember, we want to keep contamination levels down, so by using a clean piece of foil out of the roll your chances of any bacteria living on it are minimal. You could always use rubbing alcohol to wipe your foil beforehand, just to be sure. You want your mushroom to eject as many spores as possible so maintaining humidity is crucial during the printing process. Place a cup or bowl over your mushroom cap while printing to ensure it has enough moisture. The cup will also protect the area from dust and contamination. But enough babbling, let's get to it!

Equipment Required

- fresh magic mushrooms

- aluminum foil

- sharp knife

- cup or bowl

- torch lighter

- rubbing alcohol/methylated spirits

Instructions

What is the number one rule? Keep things clean and sterile! Choose a room with minimum airflow and scrub it down! Make use of a table as a sturdy surface and cover it with a clean piece of foil.

Clean all your instruments with alcohol/methylated spirits and let them dry. Tear off a piece of Aluminum foil and cut it a little bigger than the size of your mushroom cap. Heat your knife blade with the torch lighter until red hot and leave to cool. Slice the cap off the stem as close as possible to expose the gills. Place the cap face/gills down on the foil. Cover the cap with a cup or bowl and leave it for six to twelve hours. This will ensure a good, solid print. Remove the cup or bowl and lift the shroom cap carefully off the foil. Replace the cup or bowl over the print and leave for another twelve hours until the print dries. Wait for your spore print to dry before storing it to avoid moisture and the growth of bacteria. Place your spore in a foil envelope by tearing off a second piece of aluminum foil, fold it in half, and double-fold the edges. Store it in a cool, dark place. If done properly, your print can last for years.

Spore Syringe

A liquid spore syringe is not just easy, it's a no-mess no-fuss method. This is perfect for novice shroom cultivators who want to keep their inoculation process as sterile as possible. You are going to need a spore print, as explained above to make your spore syringe, so if this is your first time growing, you'll have to source some spore prints beforehand. You can also purchase a preloaded syringe online.

Essential Equipment

- spore print

- a 10-ml to 20-ml syringe

- shot glass or small bowl

- ziplock baggie

- gas torch lighter

- sterile water

- a pressure cooker

- scalpel or knife

- tweezers

Instructions

Sterilize your water and your shot glass or bowl in your pressure cooker. Lower the temperature after your cooker reaches 15 psi and leave it to boil for another half an hour. Turn off the cooker and wait until the water has cooled to room temperature. Note: You can leave it overnight to allow it to cool naturally. Your spores will die if the water is too hot! Leave your cooker sealed, otherwise, you run the risk of contamination. Once your water is cooled, heat your tweezers with your torch lighter until the points glow red hot.

Do the same thing with your scalpel or blade and your needle if not sterile. Open your cooker and remove the shot glass. Fill the glass with 10 ml of sterile water. Pick up the spore print with your tweezers and hold it over the glass. Gently scrape the spores off the print into the water. There is no real standard for the ratio, I make three to five syringes per print. Place your needle tip into the glass and suck up your spores. Empty the syringe back into the glass to make sure your spores mix properly with the water and disperse evenly. You can repeat this process a couple of times, so all your syringes have an acceptable number of spores in each.

If you have a 20 ml syringe, use 20 ml of water in your shot glass. Repeat this method with all your syringes, scraping off spores from your print and mixing them with your sterile water. Fill your syringes and leave them at room temperature for two to three days, so the spores have a chance to hydrate completely. After your spores have fully hydrated you can pop them into a Ziplock baggie and place them in the fridge. Your syringes will remain user-friendly for up to a year if stored correctly! Happy sporing!

Bulk Spawn

For you to grow in bulk you are going to need enough spawn. You will have to get yourself a spore syringe and a bag of sterilized grain (around three pounds). You can buy these bags online complete with their own injection port.

As soon as you have both the spores and the grain, you can inoculate your sterilized bags with your sterilized spore syringe needle injecting three to five cubic centimeters of spores into it.

After 14 days you should be able to see the mycelium colonizing the grain. Shake your bag after three weeks of colonization, do this gently so you don't accidentally poke holes into the bag or damage your birthing cakes.

After another two weeks, your bags should be fully colonized and you can break up the mycelium, distributing it throughout the bag. Don't open the bag yet. Give it about six weeks to colonize properly. One bag of grain should provide you with three pounds or 1.3 kilograms of mushroom spawn that can inoculate roughly 30 pounds or 13 kilograms of bulk substrate.

Strains and Species

A species is a group of organisms that have the same genetic code. A strain is a subgrouping of that species with the same genetics as well as added genes producing slight differences in how they look and feel. Strains from the same species can be crossbred to create a new strain. Many cultivators breed hybrids that aren't even documented.

Easy-to-grow mushrooms must have these four traits in common:

- They should be low maintenance.

- You must be able to grow them in your closet.

- They must be resistant to contaminants and grow in varying temperatures.

- They must be beginner-friendly to cultivate but potent enough to deliver a great trip.

I have decided to narrow down some of the most popular and easiest strains to grow for both beginner and full-blown psychonauts.

Remember that two separate batches from the same spore might have different potency.

Golden Teachers

This is a wonderful strain if you're only starting, but they are also a firm favorite among advanced growers because of its potency. Golden Teachers have a large golden cap and a wide stem. You can get quite a few flushes from one batch, and they are popular for bulk spawning.

Albino A+ Strain

The Albino A+ strain is a pale creamy white version of the A strain. Despite its name, it's not really an albino. It has reduced pigmentation with its spores generally turning purple-black when mature. As these mushrooms begin dropping their spores, their stem rings also turn black.

B+ Cubensis

The B+ Cubensis is one of the most popular strains because of its higher-than-average potency levels. It germinates quite quickly and is very resistant to cooler weather conditions and contamination. It also produces a large flush, which is excellent for beginner cultivators. It might grow a bit slower than other strains, but it can fight off infection, which makes the wait worthwhile.

Ecuadorian

This mushroom is easy to cultivate and high in strength. It produces impressive flushes and can take extreme temperature drops without too much damage. This strain originally comes from Ecuador, known for its harsh weather conditions, which might explain the strain's ability to grow and fruit using any cultivation technique. It's a good option for beginners in mushroom cultivation.

Alacabenzi

The Alacabenzi is super resistant to contamination, quick to colonize, and grows large fruits. This variant was originally found in Alabama and is considered an easy-to-grow shroom strain. Remember, even if you cultivate two separate batches from the same spore you might have differences in potency. Warning for beginners: Go low and slow.

Z Strain

The Z strain is an aggressive colonizer with loads of large mushrooms often growing in dense patches. It grows fast and produces fruits multiple times, making it a favorite for both beginner and commercial growers. This strain is also readily available to purchase.

Crop Killers

During the mushroom cultivation process, there is always a chance of encountering some problems along the way. Your shrooms might look happy and healthy one moment and then sickly and miserable the next. There are many reasons for a damaged or dead shroom crop, including contamination from pests to unsuitable growing conditions.

To help you troubleshoot and prevent your crop from being harmed, we are going to look at some of the challenges you possibly might face.

Contamination Station

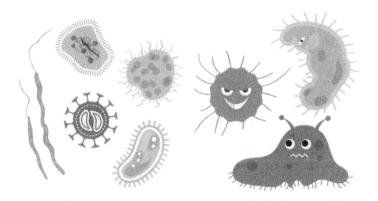

A contaminant is an impurity in the soil, air, or water that can cause major problems to your crop. If you notice signs of contamination on any of your mycelium cakes or shrooms it is best to get rid of all the infected cultures right away.

Mycelium is all white, so if you notice any other colors, it's safe to say that it has been tainted. There are two exceptions to this rule, if you notice a bluish color this might mean that your mycelium has been bruised, while a yellowish tinge indicates that the mycelium is getting old.

Germs love a sterile, clean environment because they have less competition and enemies to deal with. Mother Nature has her own way of keeping these pesky invaders from destroying all her hard work, but in unnatural environments, like your homegrown cultures, they have free reign.

Most contaminants can be categorized into three groups:

- mold

- pests

- bacteria

Mold is a fungus that grows in strands called hyphae. It can be killed by things like alcohol or baking soda. Pests are tiny insects that enjoy munching on your cultures. They can spread disease quite quickly and should be eradicated as soon as possible! Bacteria are single-cell microorganisms that reproduce at a rapid rate and can be killed by pasteurization and sterilization.

Early Signs of Contamination

By keeping an eye on your cultures, you should be able to spot contamination as soon as possible and save the rest of your cultures before they get sick, eaten, or damaged. Discoloration is one of the obvious signs of contamination. Most mold species have a specific color, so if your cultures have black, green, or gray spots anywhere on them they have been infected. Bacterial infections can be identified by slimy sections, yellow or brown stains, as well as brittle or gel-like textures on your substrate or mycelium.

Most Common Issues

We have touched on the three main culprits invading your cultures, now we will go into more detail about the most common types of contaminations.

Bacterial Blotch

Brown or yellow abrasions on the ends of your mushroom caps may mean that bacterial blotch has moved in and contaminated your culture. This bacteria spreads through floating soil particles and pollution generally takes place when your mushrooms remain wet for extended periods. To ensure your cultures stay safe, keep a watchful eye for excessive moisture and dampness. If you think your shrooms might have been contaminated, get rid of the sick ones. Lower your humidity levels and treat the rest of your crop with a 150-ppm chlorine mixture.

Mold/Dactylium Mildew

This type of mold looks so similar to your mycelium that it might go undetected until it's too late. Cobweb mold will spread like a white cotton-like blanket over your entire crop causing soft rot.

All types of mold love damp areas, so keep your shroom crop safe by lowering those humidity levels and ensuring continuous air flow circulation.

Pink Mold/Red Bread Mold

The Neurospora mold species is commonly found in agar and grain. It grows quickly and it's very difficult to kill once an infestation has started. There is no hope for your cultures when this mold attacks. The best you can do is to destroy infected crops immediately.

Green Mold

The scientific name for this killer is Trichoderma harzianum and it is an aggressive mold! It will cover your crop in a matter of days by producing green spores that cause soft rot. Green mold is very common in most households, and it should be taken seriously. Strict sanitation methods, including disinfecting your surfaces, are a must to keep this assassin at bay.

Black Mold

This is another type of fungi that grows in agar, grain, and organic substrates. Even though the species is called black mold, it comes in a variety of colors ranging from black to yellow. These strains can be lethal as they produce aflatoxins, so keep your growing areas sterile and well-ventilated!

Wet Spot/Sour Rot

This fiend likes to take over Mason jars. What happens is that the bacillus manages to survive the sterilization stage in the shape of endospores that are completely heat resistant. Common characteristics include gray slime that stinks and makes the grain look sopping wet. One way to stop this from happening is to soak your grains at room temperature for a minimum of 24 hours.

The water allows the endospores to germinate, killing them when you sterilize this time around.

Dry Bubble

This disease causes abnormal, crooked pinheads and bent mushrooms with slanted caps. The spores stick to dust particles, so try not to work with soil near your grow boxes. Flies can also spread the spores, so keep them out wherever possible.

Mites

Mites flourish in straw and manure. In the wild many mite species benefit from mushroom growth as they feed on eelworms and other mites. This species only causes mayhem. They eat the mycelium, eventually killing your whole crop. Correct sanitation and hygiene practices are recommended if you want to control these contaminants.

Fungus Gnats

These little insects love burrowing into your mushrooms and provide a nice entry point for other bacteria and diseases to join in the fun! Gnats are a whitish color when young, but adults have a more grayish, blackish tint. Rigorous sanitation is the only way to go if you want to eradicate them.

Growing Pains

Failure to provide perfect environmental conditions will also greatly impair your mushroom's growth. I'm going to teach you a bit about the most common growing challenges and how to overcome them.

Substrate

The right substrate for your shrooms is just as essential as the correct humidity and climate. Make sure you provide the preferred substrate for the species you want to cultivate. You can also use additional supplements with store-bought nutrients to boost your yield.

Moisture

Moisture is one of the most vital ecological factors when growing mushrooms. Too little humidity will cause your mycelium to dry out and die. Mushrooms that don't have enough moisture while growing will become brittle and their caps might form tiny cracks. Mist your shrooms once a day during the fruiting period and, if possible, get yourself a humidifier.

Too much moisture is just as bad. Stagnant water puddles are a perfect breeding ground for contaminants like mold. Provide enough drainage holes and never over-water your crops.

Light

Mushrooms don't like direct sunlight, but they do need some ambient light to grow properly. If you notice that your shrooms are leaning in one specific direction, it's because they are searching for light.

Pick an inside area with enough natural daylight or invest in a grow lamp if you can afford it. Outdoor crops should not be kept in heavily shaded areas or direct sunlight.

Fresh Air

Any living creature needs air to breathe. If your shrooms don't get enough oxygen their growth might become stunted or they might become deformed. Remember to lift the lid off your containers for a few minutes once or twice a day for enough air circulation.

Climate

Every mushroom species prefers a different kind of climate. Do some research to see which types of mushrooms will grow well in your area if you want an outdoor crop. Indoor growers have more control over their environment and can provide extra heat if necessary.

Shroomy Summary

- One spore equals one mushroom, but a single mushroom can produce hundreds of thousands of spores.

- Spore prints and spore syringes can provide the grower with thousands of shrooms if handled correctly.

- To prevent contamination, keep your areas, tools, and general environment sterile and sanitized.

- Make sure your shrooms aren't too wet or too dry.

- Don't place your mushroom crop in direct sunlight.

Chapter 6: Before, During, and After the Harvest

"From dead plant matter to nematodes to bacteria, never underestimate the cleverness of mushrooms to find new food!"-Paul Stamets

Your first crop of shrooms survived, and now they're ready to be dried, but when is the right time to harvest them?

As a magic mushroom cultivator, you had to ensure that your environment was set up correctly. It had to be free from any contamination and light, heat, and humidity conditions had to be 100%, and you had to be careful so as not to over-mist your shrooms. You managed to adhere to all these guidelines, and soon your pins formed into beautiful mushrooms. Success! You ended up with a bountiful harvest. Hooray! Now a new pressing matter arises. When should you harvest your magic mushrooms?

Making sure you have a thriving mushroom yield that looks just as good as they are going to make you feel, needs careful planning. They must be harvested at the right time and if you miss this window of opportunity your mushrooms will quickly go from healthy caps and stems to shrooms full of black spores.

Psilocybe cubensis, the most popular magic mushroom to grow, has about a 72-hour window for harvesting after the pinning process starts. As soon as your pins start to appear, they need to be watched with a hawk's eye as they will quickly develop into a fruiting body. Your main aim is to harvest your shrooms before the pins mature completely. Some people say three days after the pinning process begins is too soon to harvest, but as mentioned before, the older your shroom gets, the less potent it becomes.

Once your magic mushroom's veil breaks open, it will distribute spores all over the rest of your shrooms, which can become a massive problem.

So, when is the best time to harvest and what should you keep an eye out for? Well, as soon as your mushroom's cap changes from a round shape to a more arched form that hangs over the stem, it's right for the picking! Your mushroom will also become lighter, turning from a dark reddish, brown to a lighter color, and your shrooms are ready to be harvested. The veil of the shroom will begin to extend, make sure it does not open fully because this is when it will start releasing its spores.

Harvesting Step-by-Step

We know now that you have a maximum of three days after your pins form to pick them as they grow into fully developed shrooms quite fast. We also know that as soon as our shroom caps go from round to a more convex shape they are ready to be picked. Now the time has come to look at the harvesting process.

It's day three. You just woke up and ran excitedly to your grow box! As you lift the lid you notice that your four first-born baby shroom caps have opened completely, and you know that NOW is the perfect time to pick them.

You wash your hands and put on your gloves. Your hand might be shaking a bit as you grab your mushroom knife, but excitement is crashing over you like a large wave, and you can't wait to pick them! Cut the mushroom close to the stem but leave a tiny stump behind. Ta-da! You have harvested your first shroom successfully! Pat yourself on the shoulder and be proud!

If you do not have a mushroom knife, you can always pick your babies by hand. Begin by washing your hands and putting on gloves. We must always keep in mind that bacteria can't wait to get hold of our fungi, so always keep things as sterile as possible! All the tools and containers you plan on using during the harvesting process should also be sterilized properly.

You will need two fingers to pick your shrooms. Grab the base of the mushroom and softly twist the stem in a counterclockwise direction. Make sure to pull at the same time as you twist the mushroom, gently breaking the stem without damaging your mycelium cake below. If your fingers are too big, use a pair of tweezers to get to the smaller shrooms.

A second method you can try involves grabbing the base of your shroom and removing the whole stump, instead of breaking it. You can then cut the stump off afterward. Remember to be gentle as they are very delicate.

Once the harvest is complete, next you'll want to learn how to dry and store shrooms.

Drying Process

After harvesting your shrooms, you can eat them right away and enjoy the fruits of your labor! Of course, you won't be able to eat all of them at once, so your best bet would be to dry the rest. Initially, it's recommended that you first lay them on a paper towel or even a piece of cardboard for a couple of hours to dry. This will remove most of the excess moisture.

There are various drying methods, but I will show the three easiest ways.

Air Drying

This is the simplest method. The only downside of air drying is that if your humidity is not at 55% some of your shrooms might still be wet in the middle, which can obviously lead to them molding.

What's Needed:

- a fan
- dry cardboard
- radiator/heater

How It Works:

Take the piece of cardboard and spread out the mushrooms evenly on it. None of them must touch each other so ensure enough space between them. Position your fan so it blows over all of your mushrooms. If your drying area is very damp, you can put your shrooms next to or in front of your radiator/heater and position the fan to blow over them while they are being heated at the same time. Your mushrooms must have constant airflow, test them by bending the stems. If they snap, they are ready to be stored. This process will take a couple of days.

Using a Dehydrator

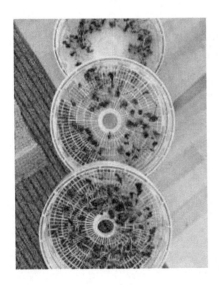

How it Works:

Many shroom cultivators swear that a dehydrator is one of the most ideal ways to dry magic mushrooms. They dry shrooms using heat and air, which decreases the risk of contamination and ensures long-term storage. You can use any food dehydrator. Just follow the instructions, but in most cases, all you must do is pick your shrooms, spread them out evenly, switch on the dehydrator, and leave them to dry. Note: Do not let your dehydrator go any higher than around 40°C (104°F)! Remember Psilocybin begins to break down when exposed to heat. With a dehydrator, you won't need more than four to eight hours to dry your shrooms. Check on them every hour just to see how they're doing!

Sushi Mat

Even though many cultivators prefer a dehydrator, there are other alternatives. The Sushi Mat system is another method you can try.

What is Needed:

- a sushi mat
- paper towels

How it Works:

Place your paper towels in a well-ventilated area with direct sunlight. Put the sushi mat on top of the paper towels. Spread out your magic mushrooms across the mat, making sure there is enough space in between each one. Leave your mushrooms to dry. It roughly takes a period of 24 hours for your shrooms to dry properly, but make sure they are bone dry. Their stems should snap when you bend them!

Storing

Your mushrooms are dry, now you'll need to store them in perfect conditions so you can enjoy them in the future! Any airtight container will keep them fresh and if you store them in a cool, dark place they should be perfectly fine.

A couple of extra storage ideas to consider include:

Vacuum Sealing

To prolong the shelf life of your magic mushrooms you should consider vacuum sealing them. By using a vacuum machine, you'll cover your shrooms in a plastic sheet eliminating all the air. This will protect them from getting damaged by any leftover oxygen.

Mason Jar

Ahh, the good old Mason jar, it has so many uses! Fill one with your dried shrooms and make sure the lid is screwed on tightly. Throw in a silica gel packet to absorb any remaining moisture, and there you go.

One major benefit of using this method is that you can have a close look at your shrooms, making sure no mold starts to grow.

Final Thoughts

Exposure to light is not good, even after your shrooms are dried. Sunlight will accelerate the degradation process. Moisture is another shroom killer and bacteria will find a way to contaminate them given half a chance. The best conditions in which to store your shrooms are cool, dark areas like a shelf inside a cupboard. Remember dried mushrooms can hold for years, and if frozen (once properly dried) they can pretty much last indefinitely.

Shroomy Summary

- Consume your shrooms fresh if you want ultimate potency.

- Mushrooms do not have to be dried if you are planning on short-term storage methods.

- If stored and dried properly, magic mushrooms have a shelf life of years; after a couple of years their potency will slowly diminish, and this is the only downside.

- Vacuum seal and store your dried shrooms in the freezer, its magic will last even longer.

Chapter 7: Forage & Feast

"...Psilocybin can offer a means to reconnect to our true nature—our authentic self—and thereby help find meaning in our lives."-Mary Cosimano

Don't fancy yourself as a hunter? Don't worry! Finding psychedelic mushrooms is not nearly as tricky as you think. They might even be hiding in your backyard, depending on where you live, of course.

Magic mushrooms are plentiful in nature and if you look in the right areas, you can get very lucky, especially during the fruiting season. Looking for shrooms is not difficult; identifying which species you found is the hard part. Magic mushrooms come in all sizes, shapes, and colors. Some are intensely potent, while others produce a milder effect. It's also important to note that many mushrooms look similar, and while some cause mild poisoning, others can be deadly. Sometimes, the difference in appearance is minimal, so you have to make sure the mushroom you're picking won't harm, poison, or kill you!

Hunting Basics

Even your top expert might find it difficult to identify a very specific mushroom strain (subspecies) and you might need specific tools to do so; a beginner will have a better chance with a genus (species) such as Psilocybe cubensis. Identifying its physical traits and analyzing its spore print are two very important steps and you'll have to get up close and personal to identify your shroom species correctly. Start with the basics and go from there.

When you finally find the magic mushroom you had your heart set on, it is time to check its physical characteristics and ask yourself some questions. Is your mushroom part of a clump that is all joined at the base, or is it growing individually? How big is your mushroom cap? How does the texture feel? Is your shroom slimy or dry? Soft or brittle? How do the gills look under its cap? Do they appear to be loosely spaced or are they close together? What color is the cap? What color is the stem?

When you bend the shroom what color does it bruise? Etc.

All these need to be answered in order to identify your strain. The next step is taking a spore print. Identifying a mushroom just by sight is never a good idea.

You can also take some pictures with your phone to identify it more professionally at home. Take a nice close-up of both the environment and the shroom, so you can show the photos to your forum or Facebook group.

Even if you do take pictures, you still need to look at the spore print. Identifying the spore print is one of the most important phases after analyzing the physical traits of the mushroom you picked.

To make your spore print you will have to cut the cap away from the stem and put the gills down on a piece of tin foil or paper. Spore prints can be light or dark, so use some contrasting colored paper, black or white, respectively. Leave the cap on the foil or paper for at least half an hour to make sure you get a nice visible print.

Whether two species look alike will depend on your knowledge and experience. Mushrooms that look identical to you could look different to me. Despite this, I added a deadly lookalike section to make you more aware of the differences.

Field Guide

I am now going to share the most common Psilocybe species, their habitat, identity, and hunting months with you.

I included an image per species to make the guide practical while reading, but I decided to keep the printed version in black ink to maintain reasonable pricing. To be clear, when printing on demand the entire book must be either in color or black ink, which would increase pricing disproportionately.

It's easy and recommended that you search for more images and videos for each one of the species to get a bigger picture of what you can find out there, simply because we will not find two identical mushrooms in nature.

Psilocybe Cubensis

Did you know that the Aztecs, called magic mushrooms "teonanacatl," directly translated as "flesh of the gods?" This genus of gilled mushrooms is the most well-known psychoactive fungi with the largest impact on the world.

Potency Level: 0.6% Psilocybin

Habitat: Psilocybe cubensis often grows near cattle, in sunny places, and mainly during the wet season. Due to the low acidity and good humidity of this soil, this species can be found on cow or even horse dung, or water buffalo manure, if we talk about Asia. They can be found in the U.S., Central and South America, Mexico, Australia, Cuba, different regions of Southeast Asia, and the West Indies. They love tropical and subtropical climates and are often found clustered together.

Caps: When young, the caps look cone-shaped (bell-shaped) but turn to a more curved shape (like an umbrella) as the mushroom ages. They are generally 1.5 cm/0.59 inches to 8 cm/3.1 inches in diameter and typically smaller when young. The center of the cap becomes a darker shade of brown and young mushrooms have a red-cinnamon-brown color that changes to a light golden brown as they get older.

Gills: At first the gills appear pale/gray but they turn to a dark, almost black color once they mature. They can look somewhat blotchy, but their edges remain white throughout.

Stem: Stems can grow up to 6 inches long and 2.5 cm/1 inch thick. Stems are hollow and white when the shroom is still young but then discolors to a darker yellow. These shrooms have a partial veil, which they shed as they mature, leaving a distinct white line around the stem. This veil can sometimes be bluish with some spots. You can find a ring or something similar to a skirt on the stem under the cap. This is the veil leftover, generally dark purple. Look for bruising around the whole body, specifically at the bottom of the stem. If there is even the tiniest scratch Psilocybin will turn dark blue due to its contact with oxygen, almost unmistakable. Bluish also appears when aging.

Spores: Sub-ellipsoidal and a dark purplish-brown color. They are covered by a partially opaque veil that becomes dusted with spores as soon as the mushroom is fully matured.

Spore Print: Dark purple to blackish brown.

Hunting Months: The best time to hunt for them is during autumn and up to two months before the hottest months in your area.

There are a few toxic/deadly look-alike species that have been mistaken for Psilocybe cubensis. Many people, for example, become intoxicated from consuming Chlorophyllum molybdites, which grow on grass, instead of dung, with olive greenish-gray spores and no blue bruising. In this book, I will try to cover the deadliest look-alikes under each Psilocybe description. There are an estimated 1.5 million species in the fungi kingdom, with 90% yet to be discovered, be aware of the risks!

Deadly - Amanita Phalloides

This mushroom is known as the Death Cap, which undoubtedly means it's a poisonous lookalike. This fungi's cap is semicircular when young but starts to flatten and expand as it matures. It is a yellowish-green color, but foragers have said they sometimes found olive to light brown colors as well. The cap can feel slightly sticky when wet but otherwise, it's dry and shiny. Fully mature caps are up to 10 cm/3.9 inches in diameter. The stem is white and can grow up to 15 cm/5.9 inches in length and to 2 cm/0.79 inches in width with a globular base. Its gills are white and don't actually reach the stem as it has a veil growing around the stem when young, covering the gills. Looking for the veil is one of the ways for you to identify this mushroom. White gills usually equal poison, so watch out for them.

Psilocybe Cyanescens

This is a potent shroom! Generally referred to as the Blueleg Brownie in the United Kingdom or Wavy Caps in America.

Potency Level: 1.68% Psilocybin

Habitat: This strain prefers to grow in rotting wood chip mulch, woody debris, and leaf litter and not grow in non-lignin-rich substrates. They are popular in California, Oregon, and Washington. Found in New Zealand, West Asia (including the Middle East), Central and Western Europe, and British Columbia.

Caps: Their caps measure between 1.5 cm/0.5 inches to 5 cm/1.9 inches in width with a convex shape that flattens out later on as they age. A key point is that the edges become wavy, therefore the American name. They have a distinct middle bump (also known as an umbo), which stays as the cap opens. The caps change in appearance depending on the moisture in the air and can stain a greenish-bluish color when bruised, which remains even after drying.

They are caramel in color but turn a chestnut-brown when they have more moisture in them. They turn a pale yellow the drier they become—a common feature in all Psilocybes. They have a gelatinous layer around them making them sticky when touched.

Gills: Gills can appear moderately crowded but loosely connected to the stem. When the mushroom is a juvenile, the gills look pale, but they begin to generate dark spots as the mushroom gets older, eventually turning a dark purple. The gills may turn bluish if touched.

Stem: Stems can be 3 to 6 mm/0.12 to 0.24 inches wide and reach a height of 3 inches/76 mm. They are chalk white (bruising pale blue), round, and fibrous. They have a partial veil covering the gills when young, but the veil fades away, leaving a pale ring around the stem.

Spores: Spores are elliptical and smooth with a dark purple or brown color. You need a microscope to identify spore characteristics.

Spore print: Blackish or very dark purple-brown.

Hunting Months: Fruiting bodies mature in the fall, so you can find them from late summer to mid-winter.

Deadly - Galerina Marginata

This mushroom does not have a wavy top, but it is very close in color. The Galerina marginata or 'funeral bell', grows in clusters, but also grows alone on occasion. It's common in South America and can be found all year round.

This cap is sticky when wet, almost bell-shaped when young, becoming more convex or flat with age. At first, this mushroom is a honey-yellow color, but as it matures it becomes a cinnamon brown. It also has a tiny veil during its juvenile period, but it disappears as the mushroom ages. Gills are broadly attached and have a yellowish color when young, but as they mature the gills turn a rusty brown. The best identifier for this toxic mushroom is the rusty brown of the spore print with dark brown bruising.

Psilocybe Semilanceata

This little baby is more commonly known as the Liberty Cap.

Potency Level: 0.98% Psilocybin

Habitat: It likes to grow in grassland, clay ground, moss, and humid areas at an altitude above 500-600 meters. It doesn't grow directly on dung but can grow in soil fertilized by dung. You can find them during autumn in North America and during the summer and autumn months in Europe, specifically in Ireland and the UK. They are common in New Zealand, Australia, and Canada. They are rare in South America, though.

Caps: Liberty Caps got their name from the distinct "hat" that they wear. They are bell-conical shaped and barely measure between 0.4 cm/0.15 inches to 2.1

cm/0.82 inches in width. The cap's edges are rolled inwards when young but unfold as the mushroom matures. When moist, they have a pale yellowish-brown color, but as the shroom matures and the environment dries out the cap turns a white, gray color with a dark edge close to the bottom. The center of the cap has a distinct point and almost looks like a nipple. They have striations that run down their caps. These markings become more pronounced as the shroom matures or with lower hydration. Wet caps feel sticky when touched. A thin, membrane-like veil can be seen when the mushroom is still young, which disappears once the mushroom has reached maturity. As the veil fades, it leaves a ring around the stem that turns darker as the mushroom ages.

Gills: Underneath the cap, gills can appear crowded, and you will notice 15 to 30 relatively close gills. Each gill is individually attached to the stem and is pale in color in the beginning; the gills look greenish gray, becoming a blackish-purple or purple-brown during maturity.

Stem: They are slender and white or pale yellow-brown with bluish-green hues at the bottom, and are inclined to get thicker around this area. They are considerably longer compared to the cap's width reaching a height of up to 3 inches or 7.6 cm and 2-3 mm in diameter. They never grow straight, the stems are bent, wavy, or curved. Additionally, they don't snap easily if bent, but they tend to bounce back.

Spores: Spores are ellipsoidal in shape and smooth.

Spore print: Dark purplish brown.

Hunting Months: Liberty Caps fruit in autumn and early winter but occasionally, have been found to bear fruit until mid-spring.

Deadly - Inocybe Geophylla

Also known as the white fibercap, this tiny mushroom is common in Europe and North America. It has a white creamy conical cap when it's young, which starts to flatten out to a more curved shape with a noticeable umbo in its center. When these mushrooms age, they do not look much like the Liberty Cap, but when young they are easily mistaken for their psychedelic cousin. One way to make sure you don't ingest a white fibercap is by bruising its flesh. This poisonous mushroom does not bleed a bluish color when damaged.

Two additional Deadly Doppelgangers:

Another close look-alike is the Pholiotina rugosa (the picture below), which has an annulus. The Psilocybe semilanceata does not have one, so check the annular zone.

The Galerina marginata, mentioned before as a lookalike for the Psilocybe cyanescens, normally grows on wood but not always, and is also a look-alike to be cautious of.

Additionally, Conocybe apala, also known as the "Milky conecap" is another poisonous lookalike.

Psilocybe Azurescens

Psilocybe azurescens, also known as the Blue Angel or Flying Saucer Mushroom, is the strongest magic mushroom, more rarely found compared to the previous genus.

Potency Level: 1.78% Psilocybin

Habitat: They prefer to grow in coastal dunes covered by grass, woodland areas full of woody debris, and even sandy soil as long as there are wood-chip areas to spawn in. They can be found growing in tight, separated clusters or they can be scattered all over the area. They have been found growing wild in the American Northwest, New Zealand, British Columbia, and Europe, specifically Germany and The Netherlands. They are easily cultivated outdoors.

Cap: The cap, depending on how much water it has absorbed, is chestnut brown to caramel color, often with bluish-black splotches, fading to pale yellow ochre when dried. It is roughly between 3 cm to 10 cm/1.2 inches to 3.9 inches wide and the young cap has a conical shape that flattens with maturity and has a distinct bump in the middle, hence the name flying saucer. It can be identified by its broad umbo right in the middle of the cap. It has a smooth, sticky feel to it when moist, as it is covered by a separate gelatinous outside layer.

The cap's edges are thin, occasionally eroded when mature, and you should be able to see exactly where the cap and the gills meet. It has a thin short-term cobweb-like white veil that it loses as the cap matures, sometimes leaving a white subtle ring around the stem.

Gills: The gills are two-tiered, yellowish-brown in color, directly connected to the stem and rising toward the cap edges. Gills are a lighter shade as they get closer to the cap's edges underneath. If the specimen is hydrated, the gills can be seen through the cap as striations.

Stem: The stems can reach a height of between 9 cm/3.5 inches to 20 cm/7.8 inches and can be 3 to 6 mm wide. They begin as a silky white color with a brown tint around the base. They turn hollow and a dirty gray or brown color with age. The stem, often thicker and curved at the bottom, may have visible tufts of mycelium at the base (silky white).

Hunting Months: These mushrooms can be found during autumn and early winter.

Spores: Ellipsoid pattern.

Spore print: Dark purplish brown to purplish-black.

Note: All parts of its body turn azure to indigo to black when handled. Like in other Psilocybes this reflects the Psilocin oxidation.

Deadly - Galerina Species

Some Galerina species are extremely toxic and as mentioned above, they look very similar to Psilocybes. Most Galerina look very similar to edible brown mushrooms too. It's difficult to describe each strain's physical appearance, but one definite way to identify the deadly Galerina species is to bruise the flesh. We know that Psilocybes bruise blue when damaged, but the Galerina species has no staining tissue. Galerina species are typically smaller than Psilocybes, but sizes do tend to overlap when the psychedelic shrooms are still young. Sometimes both these mushrooms grow very near one another, so double and triple check every shroom's physical characteristics.

Final Foraging Thoughts

Don't forget to exercise utmost caution when you go wild mushroom hunting; there are many toxic species out there and some of them are killers. The differences between magic and toxic mushrooms could be minor. Only consume what you're absolutely sure of.

Shroomy Summary

- You can use spore prints to cultivate and identify magic mushrooms.

- Take photos of your mushrooms for identification purposes.

- If you have any doubt in your mind about the shroom you picked, consult an experienced hunter before consuming it.

- Keep away from mushrooms with white gills. A rusty brown or cream color in the spore print is not a good sign either.

- Never 'over-forage'. Leave some of the younger mushrooms to mature and drop their spores, so you can come back later to pick more.

- Psilocybin mushrooms will bruise blue when they are handled roughly. The more Psilocin the mushroom has, the darker the blue reaction will be.

Chapter 8: Regulations & Restrictions

"What if, through responsible exploration with psychedelics, we free our minds? Free-thinkers are more difficult to manipulate and control, which begs the question: Why are psychedelics illegal?"–Zoe Helene

Magic mushrooms have been around since prehistoric times. They have a long history of being used for medicinal and ceremonial purposes among natives for thousands of years in most parts of the world, including the U.S. and Europe.

They became very popular in 1957 and for two decades Psilocybin was seen as the hero, while in the 70s, both Psilocybin and Psilocin became unlawful. They were listed as Schedule I drugs, according to the Controlled

Substances Act, and became one of the most heavily criminalized categories of drugs. What does this mean for you as a consumer, grower, or distributor?

Many U.S. states have started to decriminalize shrooms, which means you are permitted to grow and possess them for your personal use, but Psilocybin is still illegal to sell to someone else.

In the United Kingdom, Psilocybin falls into the Class A category of most illegal drugs.

In Canada, any mushroom containing Psilocybin is illegal. Buying spores to cultivate magic mushrooms is illegal, but if you want to buy them for "research and collection" purposes you are allowed to. Spores, spore prints, and spore syringes can be bought through the internet. Mushroom grow kits are legal and get sold on the web quite publicly.

So where is it legal to use Psilocybin?

If you live in Brazil, Psilocybin is technically illegal, but there are no laws prohibiting you from selling or growing fresh mushrooms.

Jamaica seems to be the most relaxed with its laws. It has various shroom retreats you can visit. In Samoa, Spain, or the Bahamas you are allowed to possess and consume Psilocybin. The Netherlands allows for the cultivation, purchase, and use of "magic truffles." Even though shrooms aren't legal, you can still get high by consuming their cousin instead.

Buying Spores and Other Supplies

Your first question should be: Which strain do I want to purchase? There is a wide variety of Psilocybe cubensis strains ranging from Golden Teacher (the most preferred strain for beginners) to Penis Envy (PE). There are also loads of other varieties, so my recommendation will be to do a bit of research before you make your final decision.

Your second question should be: Are the spores high quality and how will I know this? Let's say you found a site that is willing to ship all the spore prints you yearn for, ask yourself: Does this website feel legitimate? Do they mention any quality control methods? Do they have contact details that you can trace? What about reviews? Check a few mushroom forums or even their social media pages to see what other clients say about them.

Never fear to contact the vendor directly! Ask them how they retain quality control. What protocols do they have in place to keep their lab sterile? How do they prepare their spores? Etc.

Through your direct detailed questions, you will receive the much-needed information to figure out how legit their business is. If they stutter, give vague answers, or are slow to respond, skip them and move on to the next vendor!

Shroomy Summary

- Researchers that have obtained a license to examine Class A drugs are permitted to carry out clinical studies with Psilocybin.

- Mushroom spore kits are sold online legally because they do not contain Psilocybin.

- Growing Psilocybin mushrooms might be considered as manufacturing drugs and, in many jurisdictions, you can receive severe penalties if caught.

- Check your city's laws regarding the possession, cultivation, and use of Psilocybin.

Conclusion

There aren't many things that can truly alter one's personality once adulthood is reached, but it takes only a single dose of Psilocybin to bring measurable and lasting mood and personality changes. And ingested responsibly and for purposes beyond recreational use can be particularly beneficial.

The reason for these changes is all linked to Psilocybin's effect on our emotions. Mushroom trips have been described as exceptionally profound experiences, bringing about feelings of joy and connectedness to others.

They have been used for medicinal purposes among indigenous tribes for thousands of years and have been associated with amazing spiritual experiences as well as self-discovery for many. The secret to their success lies in Psilocybin, which is converted to Psilocin in the body. It is believed that this compound influences the serotonin levels in our brains, leading to an altered state with enhanced perceptions.

Magic mushrooms have so many enigmatic properties. They can demolish fear, treat mental health issues, reduce anxiety, and help with post-traumatic stress disorders. They are not just used for getting high either. Many users experience a feeling of unity and purity describing their trip as life-altering.

Shrooms will take you on a journey that you never expected! I once heard: "Shrooms don't give you the trip you want, but the trip you need." We will all experience them differently, and there are many factors that might influence your trip. Know this though, your entire perception of things around you will change. All your senses are heightened. You might even feel as if your whole reality is shifting. Time and space become altered. You may feel joyful, passionate, and more open to your thoughts. You will have mystical and spiritual encounters. They might even strip away the illusion of what you think life is. They are specific to your soul and your spirit. Who knows, taking shrooms might just be the single most spiritually significant experience of your life! At least most people who consume it say that.

Psychedelic mushrooms have an established, profound reputation as agents of healing and change. They have been regarded as drivers of personal growth. The results seen in many medical trials are promising and suggest that these magical fungi could be powerful healers.

They have the potential to spur internal development and users have mentioned lasting, positive changes in their character, behaviors, beliefs, and mindset. Keeping all this information in mind, many people believe that magic mushrooms could be a vital component to induce self-improvement and self-optimization. Your experience of feeling connected to the universe, confronting hidden parts of yourself, and delving into your subconscious could just give you the nudge needed to take the required steps to become the best version of yourself. Their benefits are finally starting to be recognized. And putting all this together, it makes sense that Psilocybin is currently the most studied psychedelic.

Magic mushrooms are used for research, therapy, spiritual enlightenment, and recreational purposes. Until the world starts to ease up on its strict laws, for most of us, using Psilocybin will remain illegal. If you do want to use Psilocybin in a non-clinical setup, it is critical that you do so responsibly. Keep factors like preparation and setting in mind and enter your psychedelic experience with good intentions. If you haven't experienced a psychedelic trip before, ask somebody to be your sitter, just in case. Keep in mind that Psilocybin has the potential to trigger hidden emotions and long-forgotten memories that you might not be completely prepared for.

Purchasing shrooms is still very risky, so try to find a supplier that is trustworthy either in person or on the web. Stay safe and don't be scared to question the products you buy.

I hope this guide has inspired you to look at Psilocybin mushrooms in an entirely new way.

Please note that Psilocybin is an illegal substance and I do not condone or encourage you to use it in parts of the world where it is against the law to do so. I do, however, realize that illegal drug use will occur, and I believe that responsible and educational information is crucial to keep users safe. For this reason, this guide has been written to ensure the safety of those individuals who do decide to use Psilocybin at their own risk.

Dear Reader

I want to personally thank you for choosing this book from among dozens out there, for acquiring an authorized copy of it and supporting my work, and for making it all the way to the end.

For so much of my life, I wanted to write a book. And as I write these lines, I am fulfilling that desire.

If you liked the content, please consider posting a review or rating on Amazon, it would mean a lot to me and it would help others benefit from my work. It is also the best way to support independent writers like myself.

Thank you.

Amazon US

Amazon UK

References

David Sanders. (2022, September 17). Image contributor: Growing process and other samples.

Ahmad, Z. (2022, March 29). Mushrooms and other psychedelics gain a foothold in Michigan. What to know. | Bridge Michigan. www.bridgemi.com/michigan-government/mushrooms-and-other-psychedelics-gain-foothold-michigan-what-know

Avalon Magic Plants. (2021, February 18). Explained: How and when to harvest your magic mushrooms. www.avalonmagicplants.com/blog/explained-how-and-when-to-harvest-your-magic-mushrooms

Brooks, M. (2022, February 18). "Magic Mushrooms" Provide Fast, Long-lasting Depression Relief: Study. WebMD. www.webmd.com/depression/news/20220218/magic-mushrooms-depression-relief-study

Canada, H. (2018). Magic mushrooms - Canada.ca. Canada.ca. www.canada.ca/en/health-canada/services/substance-use/controlled-illegal-drugs/magic-mushrooms.html

Contributor, I. (2020, September 17). 5 Health Benefits Of The Magic Mushrooms. Spa Industry Association. dayspaassociation.com/5-health-benefits-of-the-magic-mushrooms/

Cooke, J. (2021, April 30). How To Grow Magic Mushrooms: The Easy Way. Tripsitter. tripsitter.com/magic-mushrooms/cultivation/

EntheoNation. (2017). The Easy Guide On How To Identify Psilocybin Mushrooms. EntheoNation.

entheonation.com/blog/psilocybin-mushrooms-identification/

FeaturedNeurologyNeuroscience·. (2020, November 23). Psilocybin Shows Potential as Migraine Treatment. Neuroscience News. neurosciencenews.com/psilocybin-migraine-17313/

Gigen Mammoser. (2019, February 12). Mushrooms as Medicine? Psychedelics May Be Next Breakthrough Treatment. Healthline; Healthline Media. www.healthline.com/health-news/benefits-of-medical-mushrooms#The-state-of-psilocybin-research-

Growing magic mushrooms outdoors | 24High. (n.d.). Retrieved July 3, 2022, from www.24high.com/blog/125/HOW-DO-I-GROW-PSILOCYBIN-MUSHROOMS-OUTDOORS&setlang=en&ageCheckVerified=true

Hartman, S. (2020, October 18). How to Make a Spore Syringe. DoubleBlind Mag. doubleblindmag.com/mushrooms/how-to-grow-mushrooms/how-to-make-a-spore-syringe/

Lowe, H., Toyang, N., Steele, B., Valentine, H., Grant, J., Ali, A., Ngwa, W., & Gordon, L. (2021). The Therapeutic Potential of Psilocybin. Molecules, 26(10), 2948. doi.org/10.3390/molecules26102948

Magic Mushrooms & Truffles Dosage Calculator - Zamnesia. (n.d.). Retrieved June 28, 2022, from www.zamnesia.com/magic-mushroom-dosage-calculator

Mitrokostas, S. (2019, January 24). 10 potential risks of taking "magic" mushrooms - Insider. Insider; Insider. www.insider.com/are-magic-mushrooms-dangerous-2019-1#you-might-have-a-bad-trip-or-get-physically-sick-1

Moss, A. (2022, January 13). Can microdosing magic mushrooms help you quit drinking? I-D. i-d.vice.com/en_uk/article/dypynv/microdosing-psilocybin-alcoholism

Mycology, M. (2021, October 29). 5 Easiest Magic Mushrooms to Grow for Beginners. Magic Mycology. magic-mycology.com/5-beginner-friendly-magic-mushrooms-to-grow/

Nast, C. (2021, February 25). The Transformative Power of Tripping With Your Partner. GQ. www.gq.com/story/psychedelic-couples-counseling-modern-lovers

Pandika, M. (2021, October 16). Could a psychedelic ego death bring you back to life? Mic; Mic. www.mic.com/life/could-killing-your-ego-with-psychedelics-be-the-key-to-mental-wellness

Parker, B. (2020, November 17). The Easy Guide on How to Identify Magic Mushrooms. Mushroom Site. mushroomsite.com/2020/11/17/how-to-identify-magic-mushrooms/

Reality Sandwich. (2020, October 16). How to Dry Magic Mushrooms: Best Practices. realitysandwich.com/how-to-dry-magic-mushrooms/

Rivera, D. (2020, June 29). Why DIY Magic Mushroom Growers Are Gathering In A Rice Subreddit. UPROXX. uproxx.com/life/diy-magic-mushrooms-uncle-ben/

Sargent, M. (2022, February 22). How To Grow Magic Mushrooms Indoors. www.zamnesia.com/blog-how-to-grow-magic-mushrooms-indoors-n2060

Spinfuel, T. (2022, February 28). Best Ways to Take Shrooms. Spinfuel. spinfuel.com/best-ways-to-take-shrooms/

Voser, S. (2022, March 8). Magic Truffles And Magic Mushrooms: The Differences - Zamnesia. www.zamnesia.com/content/108-difference-magic-mushrooms-truffles

Wagener, D. (n.d.). Psilocybin Mushroom Facts & Information | What to Know. Recovery.org. Retrieved June 24, 2022, from recovery.org/psilocybin-mushroom/

Whalen, A. (2019, July 3). Magic Mushrooms Guide: Where Shrooms Are Legal and How To Take Psilocybin. Newsweek; Newsweek. www.newsweek.com/magic-mushrooms-psilocybin-shrooms-denver-legal-how-take-1445041

Zativo. (2017, January 16). How To Make Your Own Magic Mushroom Spore Prints – Zativo. www.zativo.com/blog/147-how-to-make-magic-mushroom-spore-prints

Image References Pixabay

Hans. (n.d.). Mushroom Pointed Tapered Bald Head [Photo]. Retrieved July 8, 2022, from pixabay.com/photos/mushroom-pointed-tapered-bald-head-228242/

Julenka. (n.d.). Sushi Chopsticks Sensei [Photograph]. Retrieved July 11, 2022, from pixabay.com/photos/sushi-chopsticks-sensei-masters-188531/

Kinkate. (n.d.). Fairytale Forest Wonderland Dream [Image]. June 29, 2022, from pixabay.com/photos/fairytale-forest-wonderland-dream-4606645/

Qimono. (n.d.). Scale Question Importance [Image]. Retrieved June 28, 2022, from pixabay.com/photos/scale-question-importance-balance-2635397/

Ramdlon. (n.d.). Legal Illegal Choose [Image]. Retrieved July 11, 2022, from pixabay.com/photos/legal-illegal-choose-choice-1143114/

RoadLight. (n.d.). Bacteria Virus [Illustration]. Retrieved July 11, 2022, from pixabay.com/illustrations/bacterias-virus-corona-disease-5545353/

Shutterbug75. (n.d.). Alone Autumn Background [Image]. Retrieved July 11, 2022, from pixabay.com/photos/alone-autumn-background-britain-1239208/

Viard, M. (2021, February 7). *Death Cap Deadly poisonous Amanita phalloides*. iStock. Retrieved September 17, 2022, from www.istockphoto.com/es/foto/death-cap-gm1300103653-392528636?phrase=amanita%20phalloides

Seijas, J. G. (2020, October 29). *Galerina marginata mushroom.* iStock. Retrieved September 17, 2022, from www.istockphoto.com/es/foto/galerina-marginata-entre-hierba-verde-y-agujas-ca%C3%ADdas-gm1282697554-380352659?phrase=galerina

Kramar, I. (2019, December 9). *Galerina marginata.* iStock. Retrieved September 17, 2022, from www.istockphoto.com/es/foto/seta-venenosa-mortal-galerina-marginata-en-el-bosque-de-llanura-de-inundaci%C3%B3n-gm1192250575-338679571?phrase=galerina%20marginata

Brezina. (2020, October 26). *Poisonous mushrooms closeup.* iStock. Retrieved September 17, 2022, from www.istockphoto.com/es/foto/grupo-de-hongos-venenosos-salvajes-inocybe-terrosos-gm1282128018-379948461?phrase=inocybe%20geophylla

AlbyDeTweede. (2018, November 26). *Psilocybe cyanescens.* iStock. Retrieved September 17, 2022, from www.istockphoto.com/es/foto/psilocybe-cyanescens-gm1070984220-286589196?phrase=psilocybe%20cyanescens

Alexander Volkov. (2021, March 22). *Psilocybe cubensis.* iStock. Retrieved September 17, 2022, from www.istockphoto.com/es/foto/el-hongo-m%C3%A1gico-mexicano-es-una-cubensis-psiloc%C3%ADdica-cuyos-principales-elementos-gm1307768764-397943479?phrase=psilocybe%20cubensis

Sergio Photone. (2022, September 17). *Hand holding small psilocybin M.* Shutterstock. www.shutterstock.com/image-photo/close-caucasian-hand-holding-small-psilocybin-2117322491

Aleksandra Duda. (n.d.). *Pholiotina Rugosa Mushroom.* Shutterstock. Retrieved September 17, 2022, from www.shutterstock.com/image-photo/pholiotina-rugosa-mushrooms-724054252

Dmytro Tyshchenko. (n.d.). *Psilocybin Psychedelic Formula*. Shutterstock. Retrieved September 19, 2022, from www.shutterstock.com/image-photo/psilocybin-psychedelic-formula-recreational-use-mushrooms-1884647911

[Serrgey75]. (n.d.). *Mushrooms Containing Psilocybin Mushrooms Psychotropic Substances Stock Photo 1831180783*. Shutterstock. Retrieved September 17, 2022, from www.shutterstock.com/image-photo/mushrooms-containing-psilocybin-psychotropic-substances-natural-1831180783

Fred JX. (n.d.). *Grow Kit Mycelium*. Shutterstock. Retrieved September 19, 2022, from www.shutterstock.com/image-photo/psilocybin-magic-mushroom-grow-kit-mycelium-2073105026?showDrawerOnLoad=true

Pyranon Sima. (n.d.). *Jar Silver Metal Lid*. Shutterstock. Retrieved September 19, 2022, from www.shutterstock.com/image-illustration/3d-rendering-jar-silver-metal-lid-1554430172

Fred JX. (n.d.). *Grow Kit Mycelium*. Shutterstock. Retrieved September 19, 2022, from www.shutterstock.com/image-photo/psilocybin-magic-mushroom-grow-kit-mycelium-2073105026?showDrawerOnLoad=true